Karla,
Best wishes
role @ MGCCC.
Donald C. Garner

Leadership Tested

A College President's Story

Howell C. Garner

ISBN 978-0-615-45505-1

GH&H Publishing

134 Bridlewood Dr.

Brandon, MS 39047

Dedication

I dedicate this publication to Dr. Author "Art" Southerland, my major professor, friend, and colleague, who has now passed on to a better life. It was through his wise counsel and encouragement that I survived the doctoral program at The University of Southern Mississippi. Art, you are sorely missed.

Acknowledgments & Thanks

The author expresses special thanks to the presidents of the fifteen public community colleges within the state of Mississippi. Their general support of the author has been overwhelming through the years. It has been a privilege and honor to have served with each of them and to call them friends and colleagues.

The author wishes to take this opportunity to say thank you to those who have in some significant way contributed to this publication. An attempt to name all of those individuals here would be futile, but there are a few special people to whom the author is indebted for advice, proofing and general counsel. Special thanks to: Ronnie Nettles, Johnny Allen, Clyde Muse, William Lewis, Scott Elliott, Jesse Smith, Willis Lott, David Cole, Eric Clark, Mark LaFrancis, Brenda Parrett, Andrea Mayfield, B.G. Allen, Ray Smith, Wayne Roberts, Wayne Stonecypher, and Dede Ginn.

Finally, I express my heartfelt thanks to my wife, Candace, who has been by my side for more than forty-one years. Her understanding of my time spent on the computer and elsewhere working on this publication is greatly appreciated.

Leadership Tested
A College President's Story

Introduction

This story is about a community college president and the challenges he faces on the job as the chief executive officer of his college. The story is fictional, and even though there are certain parts of the story that are to some extent factual, no names of characters in the story are real, nor are any of these fictional characters intended to represent real people. No exact set of circumstances presented are real to the writer's knowledge.

The story presents a series of challenges for the college president who has been on the job in a rural Mississippi community college for just over two years. For each of the challenges, he makes certain decisions and takes certain actions. At the end of the narrative there is a study guide in which the reader has the opportunity to examine the issues in detail and decide if he/she agrees with decisions and actions taken by the college president or if he/she would have taken a different approach to address each of the challenges presented.

The author is not suggesting that the decisions made and the actions taken in the story are the best ones. There is usually more than one reasonable approach to any situation. The story is intended to be an easy-to-read work of fiction with practical elements of decision-making on the part of the college president and others, which open issues for discussion. In many of the situations the reader is given the benefit of seeing the rationale of the decision-makers in the story.

Each practical situation outlined in this story provides an opportunity for individual consideration of future decision-making as a leader. Situations are also intended to provide opportunities for in-depth discussions by groups in a professional development setting.

Prologue

Fair Oaks Community College is a two-year college located in rural Mississippi on a four hundred acre tract of land that provides a spacious setting for its students. Of the four thousand students, twenty-five hundred are academic transfer students, and fifteen hundred are career-technical students enrolled in twenty-eight different career path programs. Fair Oaks was founded more than seventy-five years ago and has a long history of providing excellent instructional programs. The age of students attending the college ranges from sixteen to eighty-six; the average age five years ago was twenty-five, and now it's twenty-nine years as more adults go back to upgrade or retool their skills for the job market.

The college site has a plentiful supply of hardwoods, including the beautiful live-oak trees for which it had been named, tall & stately pines, and Bradford Pear trees. In addition, it has been landscaped with carefully planted shrubs, including beautiful crepe myrtles, to provide a wonderful outdoor atmosphere. The campus also adorns Ginkgo trees at strategic places to add the beautiful yellow and orange colors that show off God's beauty in nature as no other trees or shrubs can do. During the spring and fall each year students love to gather at various locations provided on campus to enjoy the beauty of the outdoors.

The Fair Oaks College District serves six counties as dictated by state law. The County Superintendant of Education for each county in the college district automatically serves as a member of the College Board during his/her term of office. This is the case in all college districts but one in the state. In addition, each of the local Boards of Supervisors in five of those six counties comprising the Fair Oaks' service area appoints one member to the college's governing Board of Trustees for a five year term. Also specified in law for Fair Oaks, Batson County has four board members - the Superintendent plus three appointed members. The law allowed this because Batson County is the home of the college. Finally, the College Board has the discretion under law to elect one at-large member, who also serves a five year term, from any one of the six counties. Fair Oaks has always filled the at-large position, giving the Board a total of fifteen members.

Some six years ago through a comprehensive long range planning process, the college identified the need to expand and upgrade career and technical programs, especially in the Health Occupations area, in order to meet the growing demand for personnel in those professions. During the past five years, Fair Oaks has opened three new programs and has expanded two existing programs in health occupations fields.

The college continues to be recognized for its success in all instructional programs, including the new programs that do an extraordinary job of placing graduates into medical-related occupations. The average job placement rate in the medical field has been more than ninety percent (90%) for the last decade.

The athletic program at Fair Oaks has enjoyed a great tradition of winning over the years, particularly over the past two decades. The college has always competed well in all major sports, but has been especially successful in football over the past ten years; during that time, the team has won three state championships and has finished in second place two times; it has played for the national championship two times, winning one national championship in its league; and a number of players have transferred to Division I schools where they have played well, with several of those going on to play at the professional level.

Coach Joe "Buck" West, Head Coach for football, is a twelve year veteran of the program; having earned the respect of the college administration and the fan base for his ability to get the most from all players during those twelve years. His three assistant coaching positions have generally been filled with competent individuals, but Coach West is the man in charge. Two of the assistants, coaches Randall James and Tony Gerardo, came to the college with Coach West, but Coach McKenzie "Mac" Dawson is only in his third season with the Bulldogs. He shows a lot of energy and seems to have a knack for the mental game that goes with the program. His ability to coordinate the offensive game for the Bulldogs has already won him the respect of Coach West and the two other assistant coaches. Overall, it's a solid coaching staff. The college is blessed with a great fan base for all sports.

Dr. Charles Caraway is in the third year as President of Fair Oaks. Prior to accepting the presidency, he had served eight years as a campus dean in Florida and twelve years as a district-wide administrative vice president of a two-year college in Texas. He found the two-year college system in Mississippi to be much different from what he was accustomed to in Texas in some ways, but the qualities and skills needed to lead such an institution were essentially the same. Although Fair Oaks is his first presidency, he has those qualities and skills needed to be a successful president, and he knows how to empower his administrative team members who carry out the day-to-day operation of the college. He has a high level of self confidence, but also has that rare quality of exhibiting genuine humility in dealing with other people, the sign of a great leader.

Dr. Caraway has already begun to establish a reputation of being a visionary leader, as well as a very personable and fair person who cares for the welfare of the college faculty and staff. He has gained the respect and support of the faculty and staff and has been welcomed by the communities surrounding the college. In the two years he has been at Fair Oaks, he has already made the rounds speaking to every Chamber of Commerce in the neighboring towns, and he has established a very strong working relationship with town and county governing officials during that time.

Caraway reports to the college's fifteen member local Board of Trustees, which has complete statutory authority to make final decisions for the college. Caraway has proven himself to the Board in short order. Board members like his management style, which includes carrying out his executive responsibilities in a very professional manner; and he knows when to seek approval of the Board on major policy decisions. He has endeared himself to the Board leadership as one who listens to others, but who is willing and quite able to make the tough decisions in a calm and professional manner. So far, there has been no inclination by any of the Board members to question his judgment on any issues which have been before the Board. Even in times of an overall loss in revenue and a consequent need to cut budgets across the board, Dr. Caraway has made the tough decisions and has garnered support of college personnel along the way.

Veteran community college presidents agree that a community college president faces challenges every day. It's a twenty-four/seven job. In this story President Charles Caraway faces some of his greatest challenges since taking the position as President at Fair Oaks just over two years ago.

CHAPTER ONE

Immediately following the September Board meeting on a Tuesday afternoon, Mr. Michael Bishop (Board member) asked to speak privately with President Caraway. Bishop indicated he had an item of some importance that he needed to discuss with Dr. Caraway and asked if he could have a few minutes the next day. They agreed to meet for coffee the next morning.

Caraway was curious about such a meeting. He had the impression that Mr. Bishop didn't want to meet in his office and that their meeting the next morning would be serious and somewhat confidential. He knew that Bishop had been an outstanding running back on the football team some years back and wondered if it had anything to do with a concern about the current football program, but he couldn't imagine why, since the team had finished with a 7-2 record last season and was off to a good start this season.

Bright and early the next morning the men met at the *Coffee Bean*, a downtown coffee shop. Caraway sensed that Bishop was a little ill at ease when they first met, but became more comfortable as they chatted about things in a casual manner. Finally, Bishop looked at Caraway and said, "Can we speak completely off the record?" Caraway was one who knew the importance of keeping confidence and also knew that Bishop obviously had an issue that he felt was very important, so he said, "Of course, we can talk off the record. We both want what's best for Fair Oaks; as long as what we say is in its best interest, I'm comfortable with that."

"We need to talk about the athletic program. As I'm sure you're probably aware, I played for the 'Bulldogs' back a few years ago. The regimen of the game of football taught me some principles of life I would never have gotten anywhere else. I was certainly proud of the team I played on, and I'm proud of our team this year and the winning record in recent years. We're very fortunate to have a good coaching staff and a great fan base.

A few years ago before you came as President we discussed an issue at a Board meeting regarding whether we should build a new football complex on the home side of the field – a new press box, visitors' center with all the trimmings including a snack bar, new restrooms, et cetera. As I remember the price tag was something just over $1 million."

Caraway responded, "Of course I wasn't here, but I've heard about the discussion. I remember hearing that there were a few Board members who pressed pretty hard, but there were greater needs at that time, so they backed off."

"That's right. The athletic project was tabled, but a few of the Board members were not convinced that was the thing to do – they just knew they didn't have the votes to change the direction of the college at that time."

Caraway said, "I assume from this meeting and the discussion so far that the issue is back in some way."

"Well, the issue has really never gone away. I need to tell you two things: first, I think our business should be done in the open, not behind the backs of other Board members, and second, I'm an avid fan of the sports program, but I want what's best for the college. I know we made the right decision a few years ago, and I know that we can't afford to spend money for this building program right now.

I also need to tell you the real reason we're having this discussion. I wanted to give you a heads-up that John Casco (a fellow Board member) is contacting other Board members to try to gain support to build the new facilities. The reason I know this is that he came to me and asked me for my support. He knows I'm a former athlete and that I'm a strong supporter of the team. When we talked, I said, 'John, don't you understand that we are going through a tough time right now with the possibility of major cuts in next year's budget. If we vote to build these facilities, where will the money come from?'"

"What did he say?"

"He said, 'we've managed to spend money for everything else' – he made reference to the new health science programs which cost some up-front money for renovations, et cetera. Then he said, 'why not take some of the money we have squirreled away in the fund balance to do this? We can replace it over the next few years little by little – the increase in ticket sales will help defray the cost some, and can you imagine the amount of fan support when we upgrade our facilities?"

He knows we have about $3 million in fund balance. He doesn't seem to understand that that amount represents less than eight percent (8%) of the operating budget. In my opinion spending that money just isn't fiscally responsible unless it's for an emergency, which the athletic facility up-grade is not. Again, I just wanted to give you a 'heads-up' that the next board meeting may bring a motion to open this can of worms again. I'll tell you now that I plan to vote against it, but I believe there'll be a number of Board members lined up in support of the project this time. John's done his homework on the need of the up-grade, and I believe he's going to make a strong case for doing the project."

"I really appreciate the heads-up. What advice do you have on how I should plan for this next Board meeting?"

"I really don't know the best approach, but one option is to contact Board members to explain your position before the meeting."

Caraway said, "I don't think I want to do that, at least not just yet. You said yourself that we need to conduct our business in the open at meetings, not behind the scenes."

"You're right," Bishop admitted, "I see your point. I know the Board members pretty well, and I think I can talk reason with them about the money. I certainly support the concept of better athletic facilities; I think other Board members know that. The fact that I favor the concept though might give me some additional credibility with the others. What about my making some contacts? Do you think that might help?"

"Well, I can't argue with that plan – it's totally up to you. I can't see how it would do any harm. But I would advise against getting into a heated discussion with any of them – that might negate any credibility you have when this comes up at the meeting."

Bishop asked, "What about Dr. Carson? Do you think he knows about this?"

Dr. Jim Carson has served on the Board for some twenty-seven years and as chairman for the past twelve of those years. He's a local physician who's well respected in the community and has a great wisdom for leading the Board – he's trusted and respected by other Board members.

"I don't know, but he certainly has his finger on the pulse of the Board, so I guess he could. I've felt a great deal of support from him since I became President. I think I have a pretty good relationship with him, and he's proven to me that he has good judgment, at least in every situation that I've seen him deal with. In addition, the Board seems to have a great amount of confidence in him as their leader and spokesperson. What do you think about my talking with him about this effort by Casco– in confidence, of course?"

"By all means - I certainly don't see how that could hurt. At the very least, he would have a 'heads-up' on a potential showdown at the Board meeting. Or, I could meet with him. Or, should we meet with him together?"

Caraway thought about this for a moment and realized the delicacy of the question. "You know, I think it would be best if I meet with him initially. We've got almost a month before the Board meeting. Dr. Carson may have some ideas, and he may want to meet with you before the meeting. Let me just feel him out and see where it goes from there."

"Okay, that sounds like a plan. In the meanwhile I'll talk with a couple of the other Board members that I'm pretty close to and see what they think."

Caraway responded, "That sounds good."

After the meeting with Bishop, Caraway had a quiet though busy work schedule and didn't really concentrate on this issue for the rest of the day. There were no unexpected visitors, and Judy Lockhart, Caraway's administrative assistant, was taking care of the Board minutes from the previous day. She took the official minutes for the meetings and would have the first draft ready by the end of the week for Dr. Caraway to review & approve before they were mailed to Board members. She knew how important it was to capture the correct wording to properly represent what was said in a professional manner, because she knew that the Board could speak only through its minutes.

Wednesday evening Caraway attended a called meeting of the local Chamber of Commerce on his campus and returned home late, so he really didn't give his meeting with Bishop much thought until his wife Margie asked, "How'd the meeting with Michael Bishop go, Charles?"

Margie Westbrook Caraway grew up in Gunnison, a little town near Clarksdale in the Mississippi delta, where her mother & father owned a large soy bean farm in that part of the state. Her daddy spent most days and many nights during her childhood and teenage years tending to the farm or the equipment which kept it alive. Margie had three older brothers who worked on the farm as soon as they were old enough to drive a tractor and operate other machinery. Her mama sewed for the public when she wasn't washing clothes, cleaning house or cooking to keep food on the table for her hungry crew. Margie realized later in life as an adult that her mama was a woman of rare strength and quiet resolve. She just kept going, no matter what the problems or circumstances. Although she was not a regular "church-goer", she knew the Lord and depended on him daily for her strength. You couldn't ask for a better partner in life than her mama had been to her daddy.

Margie knew the value of the dollar only too well. Since it took every penny from the sale of crops to keep the farm going year after year, she had learned the hard lessons of life on the farm – she learned to have an "I can" attitude in life. She was unusually bright as a child and made top grades in her class all through school, even though she spent much of her time in after-school hours doing chores around the house and farm.

Margie went to a university in the Mississippi Delta on an academic scholarship and graduated with honors. She met Charles Caraway at college and had a rather short courtship. But then, she knew what she wanted in a man, and Charles fit the bill – to wit, they had recently celebrated thirty-five years of marriage. As a wife of a college president, she was her husband's best friend and a loving wife and mom to their son Adam, an only child. Charles had called her "Marge" from their first meeting. Before that her daddy was the only person to use the short form of Margie. She loved her daddy deeply. And now, that love was even deeper for Charles, who had just melted her heart from the very first.

"Well, Marge, it went pretty well, but there appears to be a move on to bring up an old issue about building an athletic complex for the football stadium."

"Is that a problem?"

"Well, it could be. The cost when it came up about five years ago was something over $1 million, and will probably be at least fifteen percent above that now."

"Oh! Didn't you tell me you were concerned about the appropriation being cut again this year – can you afford to spend money for an athletic expansion at the stadium?"

"No, not really. That really isn't a viable option in my opinion, but there're some Board members who think otherwise – at least one, John Casco, has other thoughts. According to Michael Bishop, he's making the rounds among Board members drumming up support for the project. Michael thinks he'll bring it up at the next Board meeting – if not that one, then, maybe the next, as soon as he has enough support that he thinks he can get a motion passed to spend the money."

"Where will the money come from? If you don't have the money, you can't build a facility, athletic or not! Would you borrow money?"

"Well, really that's the point. We don't have the cash, but we do have money in reserve that could be spent for the project. It wouldn't be wise in my opinion, but if the Board votes to spend it, then we have a Board directive to do so. And borrowing money means we'd have a major note to pay each year for probably fifteen years."

"So, what'll you do? Will you take a position against this or will you just let the Board deal with the issue? After all, the Board's responsible for the overall operation, it's really not your fault if they make an error in judgment and spend money they don't have or that'll draw down reserves."

"I'm not prepared to take a position for or against at this point without more information and a better understanding of all the issues. I plan to talk with Dr. Carson - I'll probably call him tomorrow. I have a responsibility as the Chief Executive Officer of the college to look out for its welfare. The college's financial stability could be put in jeopardy, and that would have an effect on lots of things, maybe even accreditation, if we get in over our heads. You never know when you will need your reserves, and if there isn't enough to handle emergencies, then problems can mount up pretty fast. I at least owe it to the Board Chairman to let him know what's going on, assuming he doesn't know already, and to let him know my thoughts on the matter."

"Charles, I think you're probably right; let's go in and get ready for bed. It's been a long day. Maybe you'll feel better about this in the morning."

"You're right. Let's get some sleep."

CHAPTER TWO

The first thing Thursday morning Caraway had Judy check with Dr. Carson to find a time to meet. Dr. Carson had an opening for lunch on Friday, and Caraway had Judy juggle his schedule to allow time for the meeting. After having his schedule adjusted, Caraway began to check his email, as was his custom each morning when time permitted. He found that communication by email took some of his valuable time, but he knew it was well worth it as long as the time was used properly to provide access to him for his faculty and staff. He made it a point to attend to those important emails from his team; however, he never used this time to deal with emails which were not important to the college operation – there were always plenty of those!

Within an hour the intercom buzzed ......

"Dr. Caraway, I have a Mr. Charles Sistrunk on line one. He says he's an attorney and needs to speak with you about a dorm student."

"Okay, I'll take it."

Caraway was thinking, *an attorney regarding a dorm student – this has to mean trouble!*

"Good morning, Mr. Sistrunk, this is Charles Caraway, what can I do for you?"

"Good morning, Dr. Caraway, thank you for taking my call. I represent Miss Susie Jones, who is a dormitory student at Fair Oaks. She tells me she has been dismissed from student housing and wishes to file a complaint (*lawsuit?*). Miss Jones & I would like to meet with you at your earliest possible convenience to discuss this matter. Will you have a few moments sometime today to meet?"

Caraway was at a loss – he'd not heard about a complaint and wondered how this could have gotten to a point of an attorney calling him before he had even heard there had been a complaint!

"Can you give me any details about Miss Jones' complaint?"

"Actually, I'd rather not discuss the matter over the phone, but I'll be more than happy to reveal the details at a meeting with you."

"Very well, I'm going to put my Administrative Assistant back on the phone; she will get your number and call you back sometime later today."

"Good, I look forward to hearing from you."

"Hold the line for Ms Lockhart."

"Judy, please get Mr. Sistrunk's number so we can call him back sometime later today to discuss a meeting. Also, would you please ask him for the full name and home address for Miss Susie Jones?"

Upon hanging up the phone, Caraway buzzed Dr. Sonny Fine (Director of Admissions & Records).

"Good morning, Dr. Caraway."

"Sonny, are you familiar with a student named Susie Jones?"

"The name sounds familiar. Why?"

"I'm told she's a student here. Would you please pull her file and bring it to my office. I need to see it ASAP."

"I'll be right there."

Within five minutes Fine came in with the Susie Jones file. Caraway thanked Sonny and told him he'd return the file sometime later in the day. He looked over the file and saw nothing that looked irregular. The address matched the one Sistrunk had given Judy. Of course, Caraway knew that there was another file, the Student Services file, which would reveal much more about any type of complaint.

Caraway buzzed Dr. Robert Summerset, V.P. of Student Services

"Robert, do you know anything about a complaint filed by Susie Jones?"

"I'm not sure about a complaint, but she was dismissed from her dorm following her arrest over the weekend for having 'dope,' excuse me, 'drugs' in her room."

"Robert, would you pull all the information you have on this and bring it to my office? I'll be waiting for you."

"Yes, sir, I'll be right there."

Robert Summerset didn't remember a complaint by Susie Jones. He wasn't sure what was going on, but he knew Dr. Caraway well enough by now to know he had a problem. Bernard "Hulk" Berryman, his assistant, had handled this case with Susie Jones and had actually made the decision to dismiss her from the dorm, but honestly, he vaguely remembered that Hulk had talked with him about the dismissal. He had been very busy about that time and had just let Hulk handle it. He thought the matter was over since it happened several days ago.

Summerset tried Hulk on the intercom and got no answer, so he called on his cell phone.

"Hulk, where are you?"

"I'm at lunch in the cafeteria."

"I need you to get Susie Jones' file – I need it right now."

"Can't it wait 'til I'm done eating?"

"Nope, it can't. I need it right now – Dr. Caraway is waiting for me to bring the file to him."

"What? Okay, I'm on my way!"

When Hulk Berryman walked in Summerset's office five minutes later, he looked like he'd seen a ghost.

Summerset looked at Hulk and asked, "What's wrong? Is that the file?"

"Yeah, this is the file, but I'm afraid it's not going to be what Dr. Caraway wants to see."

"What do you mean?"

"Well, I failed to put any notes in the file as a follow-up to my meeting with Susie on Monday. I knew I forgot something that day! There really isn't much here from Campus PD either - there's the report that they found the dope, but that's about it except that she was arrested and taken to jail."

"What do you mean – that's all the Campus Police report shows? "

"I'm afraid they didn't do a very good job either."

"Let me see the file!"

When Summerset looked at the file he suddenly felt weak. It simply showed the police had done a room check and found "marijuana" in Susie's room. It did show date and time, etc., and it showed they took Susie to jail, but there was very little detail regarding how they came to look in her room, what was said by Susie or any other circumstances. There was no reference to any witnesses to anything.

Summerset said, "Okay, to sum it up..... Campus Police found marijuana in Susie Jones' room on Saturday night during a regular room check. What was the quantity? Was it sufficient for a felony or was it a misdemeanor charge?"

"It was a misdemeanor, but the amount was just four grams short of a felony."

"Okay, so they arrested her and took her to jail, she made bond and got out later Saturday night and came to see you in the Dean's office on Monday morning. Is that about it?"

"Yep."

"What exactly did she tell you?"

"She said the dope was planted – it wasn't hers."

"Did you ask her if she had any proof of that – did it belong to her roommate?"

"Yep, I did ask, and she said it didn't belong to either of them. She claims one of our officers planted the dope in her room."

"Then what?"

"Then I told her she could go get her things from her room, she was out. That was according to the policy found in the Student Handbook. That was final."

"That's it?"

"That's it. You want me to go to Dr. Caraway's office with you?"

"No. He didn't ask for you, but he may want to see you before the day's over."

"Do you think I screwed up here? I was just following policy – that's what the Student Handbook says plain and simple – if she has drugs in her room she's violated school policy – 'no drugs on campus!'"

"Well, Hulk. There's only one thing – there's an appeals process – she has a right to appeal your decision – that's found in the same handbook you mentioned!!"

"You mean, we might have to let her back in the dorm?"

"Somehow, I don't think that will be our biggest problem. I think we could be in big trouble here. Keep your fingers crossed - but while you're waiting on that call from Dr. Caraway, you might want to try to make some notes as well as you can from memory so we've got something to fall back on if this thing gets blown out of proportion. And, when you're done with that, you might also want to review the Student Handbook."

"How did Dr. Caraway get involved in this anyway? Has she been to see him?"

"I really don't know, but I have a feeling I'm about to find out. Be available if we need you on short notice."

"Okay."

Dr. Summerset headed to Dr. Caraway's office with the file, such as it was.

When Summerset arrived at the President's office, he was not his usual "upbeat" self when he greeted Judy.

"Judy, Dr. Caraway asked me to bring over a file. Would you tell him I'm here please?"

"Dr. Caraway, Dr. Summerset is here."

"Send him in."

"Hello, Robert. Come in and have a seat. That the file on Susie Jones?"

"Yes sir."

"Let me take a look."

Dr. Caraway opened the file and examined its contents – it didn't take long! He then looked up at Robert for a long moment.

"This all there is?"

"Yes sir, I'm afraid so. "

"You mean we dismissed a girl from Meander Hall and all we have is the report by Campus Police that we arrested her for having "dope" in her room and took her to jail that night – when was this (looking at the file)? Saturday night? Did she spend the weekend in jail?"

"No sir, she made bail – for a misdemeanor it wasn't a lot. I'm just as upset over this as you are, sir. We dropped the ball."

"You're not as upset as I am over this, yet!! You see, I got a call from an attorney that Susie Jones is getting ready to sue us over this – and it appears we probably deserve it!"

"Sir? You mean this may go to court?"

"Yes, it could, but we're going to do our best to rectify the situation before that happens."

"But sir, I think Susie is guilty as sin! According to Hulk, she claims that one of our officers planted the drugs in her room. You know they didn't plant them! So how else did the drugs get there?"

Caraway interrupted, "Well, I sure would hope they weren't *planted*, but what have you done to check out her story? Have you talked with the officers or to the chief, who reports to you by the way?!"

"Well, sir, I didn't want it to appear that I was accusing the officers of any wrong doing. It's hard to get good officers to work for what we pay them."

"Robert! It's your job to know the facts as well as you can before we take adverse action against a student or anyone else. You're expected to get the facts - the only way to do that is to talk to the people involved. Who was on duty that night – our regular officers or reserve (part-time)?"

"I don't know sir. The report was signed, but I didn't recognize the signature."

"Well, don't you think you need to know these things? How about the appeals process? Did you advise Susie she had the right to appeal this decision to me?"

"Well, sir, I really didn't have a chance to do that sir. You see, Hulk had read the Student Handbook to say that if drugs were found, she was to be dismissed from student housing. That was final. She didn't appeal to me."

"*What?* You don't mean to tell me she wasn't even given the right to appeal to you? Is that what I'm hearing?"

"Yes sir, I'm afraid so."

"Get Berryman over here right now!"

When Hulk Berryman got the call from his boss, he didn't need to see Summerset's face – he could feel the electricity over the phone. He knew he was going into the lion's den. Upon his arrival, he was told by Judy to go in - that they were waiting on him.

As Berryman entered the office, Caraway said "Good morning, Mr. Berryman, have a seat."

"Good morning, Dr. Caraway."

"Why don't you tell me the facts related to the situation involving Susie Jones. I don't want opinion, just the facts and exactly what happened – don't leave anything out."

"Well…." Hulk Berryman began to relate the facts as he remembered them. It helped that his boss had told him to write notes for the file as best he could remember – he had had to jog his memory when doing that, so he could now relate the facts fairly well. That didn't stop him from sweating – he felt hot and cold at the same time – he felt like he was in a trance walking through a tunnel. He could see the other end of the tunnel, but he didn't have a clue what he was going to find there as Dr. Caraway and Dr. Summerset just sat looking at him with great intensity.

Berryman thought he'd wake up from this dream any minute. Except he didn't!

When Berryman finished, he felt a little better. As a matter of fact, he had found some new faith that he was going to survive. He had confessed his sins and had been very honest and told it like it was. He'd always heard that it helped to "bear your soul" – he felt that he'd done just that. When he would later look back on this experience, he would say that he may have had a "salvation experience" – he had felt weak beginning with the knees and working quickly up to his stomach - he realized he couldn't make it through this without the Lord walking beside him. He *must have!*

"Mr. Berryman, I appreciate your relating these facts as you remember them and the candor in which you did so. I believe from hearing you talk about this that you now realize how serious this situation is and how badly you have 'screwed up,' as the old saying goes. First of all, you've caused both Dr. Summerset and me to have to spend valuable time to work out a solution to this "mess" you've caused, but most importantly, you've put this college in a potentially embarrassing position – our reputation is always on the line, and it's up to all of us to be careful to act in such a way that we don't jeopardize that. We're stewards of the college's good name and reputation for now and for years to come. Your actions may cause a blemish on that good name – that's bigger than you, Dr. Summerset and me. Do you understand that?"

"Yes sir. I want to apologize for making this mess, and I want to do anything I can to help make it right."

"Very well Mr. Berryman. Please wait outside - I need to speak with Dr. Summerset for a moment."

Robert Summerset was a little proud of how well Hulk Berryman had handled the situation and felt that the worst was over. Little did he know his turn was coming very soon.

"Dr. Summerset, I can't tell you how disappointed I am with this whole situation. I, as President, cannot be everywhere at once, and I can't possibly make all the decisions which are required to run this institution. However, the buck stops with me, so what I have to do is 'delegate' to others who can be trusted with decision-making ability and the authority to carry out decisions on a daily basis in the interest of taking care of the business for this college.

When you were named V.P. of Student Services by a president who came before me, he delegated some serious responsibilities to you for making important decisions which pertain to students at this college. When I became President of the college, I affirmed those responsibilities which were yours. I even met with you for a very straight forward discussion of how important your job was to this institution in carrying out those responsibilities. You remember that meeting?"

"Yes sir."

"This morning I see that you have totally failed to carry that load in regard to this particular situation. I'm disturbed by your failure to be a good steward of your responsibility; much more than I am about the potential lawsuit from Susie Jones. You have abdicated your duty to someone who has totally left it undone and made a genuine mess for us all.

Let me ask you, what do you think I should do about this situation?"

Robert could hardly find words to answer. He certainly didn't know the answer.

"I don't know sir. I realize now that this responsibility has just been given a lesser importance than it's due, and that's entirely my fault. I don't know what you should do, but I'm willing to do anything you say to try to make this right."

"Dr. Summerset, I'm going to have Mr. Berryman come back in, and I'm going to give the two of you an assignment. The assignment will be for the two of you, but YOU will be responsible for that assignment being carried out. You understand that?"

"Yes sir."

"Judy, have Mr. Berryman come back in please."

When Berryman was back, Caraway began, "Gentlemen, it's obvious to me that you need to get a better grip on your duties in the Student Services Division and how it relates to the reputation and to the overall welfare of this college.

I don't know the final disposition of the Susie Jones situation; you're certainly not off the hook on that, but right now I want you to concentrate on what went wrong to get us to this point. And then I want you to develop a plan to be sure it never happens again. In that process I want each of you to provide me with a prioritized list of your duties. I'll stop short of asking you to memorize the Student Handbook, but make no mistake, you are to be familiar with that document from cover to cover; not only that, I want you to always be on the lookout for ways to make that document better. It's the responsibility of the Student Services division to keep that information up-to-date. It's time you took that responsibility seriously.

I'll expect your response to this assignment by Wednesday of next week. I'm giving you more time than is needed because I want you to give this some serious thought. It's also your responsibility to follow procedures so that you avoid this very kind of thing! Any questions?"

They said almost in unison, "No sir."

"Okay, get going."

As they left the office, Dr. Caraway was very aware that his plan might not work to get these men back on track. They both seemed sincerely sorry for the problems they had caused, but he wasn't sure they could change their ways enough to get the job done. He wondered why he hadn't seen this problem before now. It's clear that Robert Summerset had simply left some things up to Berryman and that he hadn't given them serious attention. Priorities were certainly not in order! Caraway wondered how many problems had been missed at Fair Oaks simply because students hadn't gone to the trouble to assert their rights.

As Caraway pondered the situation, he wondered if he might have been a little too tough on Summerset & Berryman; then he remembered that a mentor president once told him, "...everybody needs an --- chewing once in a while. Both the 'chewer' and the 'chewee' need the experience." He also remembered what one of his professors had said in a leadership class, "....a little calculated anger is sometimes needed to get the attention of folks." Caraway was convinced that both of those tips had a place under the present circumstances.

The meetings with Summerset and Berryman had taken most of Caraway's morning, and Caraway reminded himself that he needed to update Leon Burchfield, the Board attorney, on the Susie Jones matter. He knew one thing for sure - he needed to get Mr. Burchfield involved in this before meeting with Mr. Sistrunk. The issues were getting fairly complex, and it was going to be a legal matter now. He just hoped there could be a practical solution to this mess.

He kept thinking about the few facts that he did know about this situation. He felt that something was "wrong with this picture;" it was a little odd that Susie had so much marijuana in her room. He had gotten to know every officer who worked for Campus Police, including the part-time people, and he didn't for a minute believe one of the officers had planted drugs. That only left one thing in his mind. He made a call to Butch Howard, his Chief of Campus Police.

Caraway's discussion with Chief Howard revealed that the "room check" in the dorm had been prompted by information from a confidential informant that Susie was using drugs on campus. A dormitory room check was not unusual and was simply a way to get into Susie's room to do a visual search. It had paid off. The chief verified that they had found visual evidence of drugs and had performed an arrest. He also confirmed that on going back into her room later with a warrant, they found twenty-six grams of marijuana, among other drug related items.

Caraway told Chief Howard about an idea he had and asked him to check on a couple of things. He asked him to get back to him within a couple of days.

"Judy, would you please get Leon Burchfield on the line for me. I really need to talk with him as soon as possible."

"Yes sir."

A few minutes later Judy buzzed Caraway.

"Dr. Caraway, Mr. Burchfield's not in his office. His secretary put me through to his voice mail, and I left him a message to call you ASAP."

"Thanks!"

Caraway dialed a cell number he had for Burchfield and left a message there. Within thirty minutes he had a call back from Burchfield on his own cell phone.

Dr. Caraway had learned that a college president needed to have a very clear understanding with the college attorney that if he needed the attorney, he needed to be accessible in a reasonable amount of time. Likewise, Burchfield knew that this call was important, not urgent in the absence of that indication on the voice mail, but nevertheless important. He didn't interrupt a meeting that was about to conclude, but he made the call as soon as he was free.

"Dr. Caraway, how can I help you?"

"Mr. Burchfield, thanks for returning my call. I've been contacted by Mr. Charles Sistrunk regarding a complaint being filed by a dorm student, Susie Jones. I've checked into the situation and have some information about what happened to initiate the complaint. I really need to discuss this with you before I talk to Mr. Sistrunk in any detail."

"Of course!"

"Mr. Sistrunk wants to meet with me – today if possible, but I think that's out of the question now. Anyway, I need to bring you up to date. What's your schedule look like for a meeting?"

"I can meet late this afternoon, say about 5:30. I've got a case going and have to put in some hours tonight, but I can take a break for dinner. I should be able to carve out an hour or so. That work for you?"

"Sure. I'll put Mr. Sistrunk off 'til after I've brought you up to date. Where do you want to meet?"

"How about Louise's Sandwich Shop downtown? You know where that is?"

"Sure, I'll see you there at 5:30."

CHAPTER THREE

Dr. Caraway and Mr. Burchfield met as planned that afternoon. Caraway had taken the file with him, and he did his best to describe the conversations with Summerset and Berryman for Burchfield. He certainly didn't feel comfortable with the facts, or rather the lack of documented facts, related to the action that had been taken by Hulk Berryman on behalf of the college. He hoped that the Board attorney would tell him something that would make him feel better, but he'd been around long enough to know they had a problem, potentially a serious one.

"Dr. Caraway, my guess is that you've had a very interesting morning from what you've told me. Let me be very candid with you.

Oh boy, here comes the bad news!

There's a chance we can work out something to get you, the college, out of this mess, but if I can, it won't be because your administrative team has done its job. This is about the worst case of dereliction of duty I've ever seen. I mean, first the Assistant to the VP doesn't give the student her right to appeal – it even appears he thinks he has the final say on this matter; then he does absolutely nothing to check out the facts of the case, and of course he writes nothing for the file so there's no reference as to what actually has been done. Does he realize how badly he screwed up on this?"

"Mr. Burchfield, I'm dealing with those issues. I take responsibility for the fact that the administration has a very weak case to have taken any action at all. My major question now is how vulnerable are we to a costly lawsuit, and what can we do to avoid it? In addition, I have a concern that we may set a bad precedent here by having to let this girl back in the dorm, when I really believe she is guilty of the drug charge."

"I understand. As I said a moment ago, maybe we can work something out. Sometimes there're things which don't come out until the lawyers sit down to discuss the legal issues."

"Okay, Let me ask you this - is it too late to provide Susie with due process, or do we need to plan to admit a mistake and let her back in the dorm?"

"I was going to suggest that you have Dr. Summerset get a message to Susie by whatever means you use to communicate with students – ask her to come to his office to meet on this matter. Now, don't be surprised when she doesn't – I'm sure Sistrunk has already told her not to meet with any of you. This is just a way on our part of trying to show good faith – we want to try to correct the problem that has been caused by Mr. Berryman. By some stretch, if she does show up, be sure Dr. Summerset knows to provide her with the due process – let's not blow a second chance if we get it."

Caraway responded, "Okay, what do you think at this point?"

"Let's see what Mr. Sistrunk has to say. This really is a mess, but we may be able to get out with minor damage."

You just don't know how big the mess is, but if my theory pans out, we'll do better than get out with minor damage.

Caraway wanted to be sure there would be quick follow-up by Burchfield, so he asked, "You'll let me know after your meeting with Sistrunk?"

"Sure."

Upon ending the meeting, Burchfield admonished Caraway not to discuss the case with anyone – and to be sure to tell Summerset and Berryman emphatically not to talk to anyone, he emphasized "anyone," about this.

Caraway felt somewhat better after meeting with Burchfield. He considered whether he should meet with Jean Webster, Director of Public Information, to give her a heads-up on the possibility that the college would be in the news about the arrest, and maybe a lawsuit. He wasn't worried about the confidentiality issue with Jean, since she had to know things off limits to others more times than not. He had never known her to misuse information, and he trusted her without reservation.

The news about Susie Jones' arrest would definitely be in the police report column, but he doubted it would get any more attention. Arrests of students were not common, but this one didn't seem any different from others that had taken place – and they didn't usually draw much attention. So, he decided to wait to see how the meeting went between Burchfield and Sistrunk before bothering Jean with this. He'd have time to fill her in if he got bad news from Burchfield, and it just might go away without any major public attention.

He headed home to settle in for the evening. He could use a tall glass of ice tea at the end of this day!

Margie walked around to the side of the house when she heard him drive up.

"Charles, I'm sitting on the deck out back just relaxing after my dinner. I made a fresh pitcher of tea. I'll pour you a glass while you put on something more comfortable."

"Marge, that sounds great - I'll be right there! You're a sweetheart!"

Charles took off his coat and tie and joined Margie on the deck.

"Charles, tell me about your day. Weren't you going to call Dr. Carson to set a meeting today?"

"I'm meeting him for lunch tomorrow."

"Were there any new developments today?"

"Marge, you know how I've told you that some days you go into the office with your day all planned out and then something comes along to put everything on your list on hold?"

"Was this one of those days?"

"Oh yeah! My day has been spent dealing with a situation which I knew nothing about until nine o'clock this morning. And the bad thing is that it could be just the beginning."

"Charles, what on earth are you talking about?"

"Well, I got a telephone call this morning from a Charles Sistrunk."

Charles told Margie the story of the events of the day and how he had met with Leon Burchfield, the Board attorney.

"Well, you did have one of those off the chart days, didn't you? Do you have any follow-up to do tonight or can we just sit here and relax for a while?" She poured him another glass of tea.

"Everything's going to be fine, Marge. We'll take our licks if we have to, and then we'll get it right next time. But I may have some tough personnel decisions to make in the meanwhile."

Friday morning was uneventful for Caraway, but he had a lot of catching up to do on email, messages, correspondence and notes he needed to make for his files. He also proofed the Board minutes – there were very few changes to be made before mailing. He was able to clear his desk once again for the weekend, of course except for those major items which were still pending. He left for lunch at 11:45 AM and told Judy not to forward any calls unless they were urgent. He didn't want to be disturbed while meeting with the Board chairman.

"Thank you for allowing me to meet with you on such short notice, Dr. Carson."

"No problem at all. How are things going? "

"Fine. We have a lot going on right now, but generally things are moving along very well. Our new programs in health occupations are really doing well, and the football team is undefeated so far."

"Good. Are you finding any time for golf these days? The weather has been just perfect."

"Not really. I guess it's a matter of priority, and my priorities have been taken up with other things lately, but I hope to play next weekend. A friend's coming down from Memphis for the weekend on his way to Pensacola, and I've promised to get him on a good course."

"Good! You need to get out – you and I both know that your job can become overpowering if you let it take over. You need some time for relaxation!"

"I'm afraid I know the principle better than I practice it, but I keep hoping to do better."

"Good! Charles, if I could take just a moment before we begin..."

"Sure Dr. Carson."

Dr. Carson began with a bit of nostalgia. "You know, Fair Oaks is a special place for a lot of people. Betty and I met here some forty-five years ago. Little did I know that I was going to get a wonderful wife as the better part of my college experience. Fair Oaks has meant so much to so many people through the years, not the least of which, me and my entire family!

And now I'm proud to be a part of the Board, and I'll do anything within my power as an individual and as a Board member to help it thrive and keep providing educational opportunities for people who wouldn't have those opportunities otherwise. I sense that you've already become attached in a personal way to this place in just a little over two years."

"Dr. Carson, first, I feel honored to work for an institution that has such a great tradition of providing opportunity for those who wouldn't otherwise have it. And I appreciate your leadership on the Board and your willingness to be a sounding board for me. You're right – I have become attached to Fair Oaks in a personal way. I understand how special it is to others, because it's already special to me. I sometimes have to fight the urge to treat it as 'my' college, knowing full well it isn't. But I do realize that I'm at the helm and I'm responsible to the Board and to the college to steer the ship on a course that continues our great success."

Carson got down to business, "Charles, I sensed from Judy that this meeting was about something important. So what's on your mind?"

Caraway didn't hesitate, "I need to share something with you today that may be rather sensitive – you'll know that probably better than I after you hear what I have to say.

I'm sure you recall a time a few years ago before I came as president that an issue was raised about building new facilities on the home side of the football stadium."

"Of course. As I recall there was a good bit of support for that project, but the motion to build those facilities was tabled until we could determine how to pay for it."

"Well, it appears that the issue may come up soon, maybe at the next Board meeting."

"Really? I haven't heard any more about the project since we tabled it five years ago."

Caraway said, "A Board member has approached me to give me a heads-up that another Board member is apparently drumming up support to bring the item back up and approve building the facility."

"This is the first I've heard of such a move. Tell me more."

"There really isn't much to tell. I just wondered, first, if you knew, and if not I wanted to give you a heads-up as well."

"Are you at liberty to tell me who the Board member is that is politicking for support? Well, first, should I know who the Board member is that has shared this with you? I assume from our discussion that you don't have the information from other sources."

"That's right – I only have the one source. Michael Bishop shared this with me, and John Casco is the Board member that's looking for support for the project."

"Why am I not surprised? I've known John for a long time; as a matter of fact, he was a student athlete here after I got appointed to the Board. I remember he was a pretty good defensive end for our team back then. He was a strong proponent when this issue came up before."

"Dr. Carson, I'm still learning the Board members, but Mr. Casco seems to have the college at heart from all indications since I've been here."

"Oh, yes, I think he does! He's a good man, but he sometimes gets overanxious to get things done. He took it pretty hard when we voted not to build the new athletic facilities. And he definitely has his focus on 'athletics'.... maybe I should say the 'football,' program. I probably should have seen this coming, but it's been almost five years, and I thought he had accepted the idea that this would have to wait a while. "

"Michael and I talked a little about what might have triggered this new effort."

"I was about to ask if you had any idea what could have changed to bring this back to the surface."

"Michael indicated that John made a comment about how the college had spent money for 'everything else' and made reference to the new programs in health occupations. So, it looks like that might be what triggered the new effort to spend money on athletics."

"Did John say where he thought we'd get the money?"

"Well, yes, he did. And really I guess that's what concerns me the most about this whole thing. He mentioned the fact that the college has a reserve fund that could be used."

"Charles, you haven't been here long enough to remember when we had to borrow money to make payroll at certain times of the year while the college was waiting for a reimbursement from the State Board, but I'm confident that you understand the importance of having that reserve fund at an acceptable level for emergencies. Do you remember off hand what that fund is now – it must be close to $3 million."

"I looked at it after my meeting with Michael. It's just under $3.5 million."

"Good, that's a little better than I remembered. I've forgotten just how much the athletic facilities would cost, but it seems it was about a million dollars. Have you looked at that number?"

"Michael said the number was about $1.1 million five years ago. I think you can add about 15% to that and be pretty close. Fifteen percent would put the cost at about $1.3 – that's a ballpark figure."

"So, we are talking about potentially dropping our fund balance to $2.2 million, give or take."

"That's the way I see it. We could survive that reduction under current conditions, but what worries me is that the state appropriation is very likely to be reduced again this next year by up to 5%. We stand to lose close to ¾ million dollars if that happens. Tuition would help make up the difference if we had a healthy increase in enrollment and had no major increase in costs as a result of that enrollment growth. However, it's never wise to budget for an increase in enrollment growth just to balance."

Dr. Carson is thinking....*Charles seems to have done his homework in a short period of time. Besides that, he seems to really be thinking of the college's best interests. It would be easy for him to just say "this is a Board decision, and I'll live with that." He recognizes he works for the Board, but he also seems to feel a responsibility to try to provide professional leadership for us by making sure we don't step off the deep end. He's only been here for just over two years, and he has a good grasp on this issue, partially thanks to Michael Bishop, but mostly because Charles did his homework. Yep, I think he has developed a "personal" attachment.*

"Charles, when did you meet with Michael Bishop?"

"We talked briefly just after the last Board meeting, but really didn't get into the issue until the morning after the Board meeting. That's when we both decided I needed to discuss the issue with you."

"Charles, I appreciate your bringing this to my attention. I think we will just see what happens and be ready to have a good discussion about the pros and cons when the time comes. You know, we have a great Board of Trustees, and they're accustomed to putting their priorities in the right place to act in the best interest of the college. Let's just let this play out and see what happens.

In the meanwhile I suggest that you have a very private discussion with Joe Biggers, (VP for Finance) and bring him up to speed on the matter. You need to have Joe ready to provide solid information on our financial picture at the meeting when this issue comes up. Let's be prepared, but let's not appear to be 'loaded for bear' when the time comes; it's not an unusual thing for a VP for Finance to have good up-to-date information on the college position, beyond what the usual report shows the Board."

"Yes sir. Thanks for listening, Dr. Carson. I feel better just having talked with you about this issue. I'll bring Joe up to speed and get him to pull some information together before the Board meeting."

"Great, now I've got some patients that I don't want to keep waiting. You have a good day, Charles!"

"You too, Dr. Carson."

CHAPTER FOUR

As it turned out, Caraway had a full afternoon after his meeting with Dr. Carson and didn't have a chance to meet with Joe Biggers. Since he had three weeks before the next Board meeting, he didn't feel the need to rush such a meeting.

Caraway had an unexpected visitor that afternoon. Harry Johns, an alumnus of Fair Oaks who now resided in Buchanan, Michigan dropped by to visit with Joe Biggers.

Judy buzzed and said, "Dr. Caraway, I know you're busy, but there's a gentleman here who would like to take just a moment to speak to you. He graduated from Fair Oaks twenty years ago and was just dropping by to see Joe Biggers as he passed through. He and Joe grew up together. Joe wants you to meet him."

"Sure, I'll be right there!"

Joe did the introductions. "Dr. Caraway, this is Harry Johns. We grew up together in Ackerman, Ms. – we kinda lost track of each other after high school graduation – we haven't seen each other in over twenty years."

"Nice to meet you, Harry - good of you to stop by to see Joe. I'm sure the two of you have enjoyed trading stories about the 'good ole days'!"

"Oh yeah! It's been fun to visit and reminisce about those days, and Joe treated me to lunch in the Faculty Dining Room."

"Dr. Caraway, I thought you'd want to meet Harry. Actually, he's an alumnus of Fair Oaks and just wanted to meet the college president! Would you guys excuse me? I have a meeting with some staff members in five minutes. Harry, it sure was good to see you – thanks for dropping by – be safe as you go back to Buchanan. Let's try to stay in touch."

"Let's do! Thanks for your hospitality Joe, I'm really glad I took the time to drop by. You look great!"

Dr. Caraway welcomed the opportunity to meet with an alumnus, "come on in for a moment, Harry, I know you're probably ready to get on the road, but it's not often we get a visit from an alumnus that far from home."

"Well, I won't keep you long, but I did want to meet you and tell you how great a job you're all doing; I get the alumni magazine and keep up with things at the college; that's how I knew Joe was here. Fair Oaks means so much to me. I don't know how I would've gotten an education without Fair Oaks."

"Great to hear you say that. I've only been here just over two years, but I've met so many people who have a similar story about Fair Oaks."

"You know, I'm so proud of Joe – how he's really made something of himself."

"Well, I'm sure he had some opportunities that he took advantage of along the way. I know we're glad to have him taking care of our finances here at Fair Oaks."

"Joe's a great guy - and we were the best of friends growing up. He just got into a little trouble as a teenager, but it has all turned out great."

Caraway, a fairly intuitive guy, sensed there was something more to this story, so he gently probed, although with some reluctance. All he needed about now was to find skeletons in Joe's closet. But... he probed nevertheless.

During the conversation that followed, Caraway found out that as a teenager, Joe had been arrested and convicted on a charge of possession of an illegal substance, enough to merit a felony charge; however, Joe had fully cooperated with the law, and his father, an influential member of the community, had been able to get the conviction expunged by the local judge.

After a much longer visit than expected, Caraway finally explained that he had to get back to his work. He thanked Harry for dropping by for a visit and wished him well on his journey home.

Caraway could not get this news off his mind. On top of all else that was happening right now, he didn't need more problems, but this problem was one that had to be settled in his own mind, since Joe Biggers was such an important part of his leadership team. He had to be able to trust him. So, like it or not, he did some checking.

Since this issue had never been mentioned to him, Caraway decided to look at Joe's personnel file to see if there was any reference to this situation at all. The college's application for employment Joe completed some ten years ago had a question regarding whether the applicant had been convicted of a felony. What he found was that Joe had answered "no" to that question. He also found that nothing was mentioned about this in any of the personal reference checks that were made on Joe before employment. There was absolutely no reference to any problem of this type in the file, but Caraway did find a reference letter In the file that had a vague comment about Joe, that said "....and I am so glad Joe is getting a chance to really make something of his life." He pondered that comment some and wondered if that's what the person might have been referencing, but there was nothing else in the file indicating any type follow-up to that comment by the person checking references.

As far as Caraway knew, there had never been a problem with Joe using illegal drugs of any type. As a matter of fact, he had been an outstanding member of the community for the past ten years.

Caraway closed the file and returned it to the locked personnel cabinet in the walk-in vault and sat down to take care of some of the paperwork Judy had brought in a while ago.

Caraway returned the signature folder and other material to Judy and noticed it was almost time for her to leave for the day, so he told her to go ahead early and close the door so he wouldn't be disturbed. He often used the late afternoon as a time to think about matters that were on his mind. He had several matters which merited his concentration, but today he just wanted some quiet time to think about this latest thing with Joe Biggers.

About 6:00 o'clock Margie called Caraway on his cell. When he heard her special ring, he realized he'd stayed later than usual without letting her know, especially on a Friday. She was just curious about when he'd be home.

When Charles got home about 6:15 Margie had a glass of tea waiting for him. They sat on the deck overlooking the catfish pond behind the president's home and just relaxed. Caraway often enjoyed some late afternoon fishing for catfish in the pond behind the house, but today wasn't one of those days. He and Margie both enjoyed the peace and quiet on days when the weather wasn't too hot or too cold. Today was wonderful!

"What kind of day did you have, Marge?"

"Oh, it was kind of quiet and peaceful. I did a little housework and read some in my latest book. How about you?"

"Well, it was a pretty full day. I had lunch with Dr. Carson – we discussed the John Casco thing about building athletic facilities."

"What did he think?"

"Well, first, he didn't know about John Casco drumming up support for the building project. I'm glad I met with him – as Board chair, he doesn't need to have a surprise like that at a Board meeting. He took the whole thing rather calmly – he's well respected by the Board, and whatever happens, I think they'll listen to reason."

"Does he think the college should spend the money for the project?"

"My impression is that he doesn't think so. He seemed to feel a certain confidence that I'm missing on this whole thing. He knows the Board pretty well; I think I just have to trust his judgment. Basically, he said 'let's see what happens.'"

"Good! I think you can take a little pressure off yourself now, don't you think?"

"Perhaps. I do feel better knowing that he's up to speed on the whole thing."

"Are you going to call Michael?"

"No, not just yet. My guess is he'll call me to ask how the meeting went. I'll be glad to share that, but I think I'll just leave things alone at this point."

"Okay. So let's just relax a bit – it's been a rather long week – you deserve it."

"It has been a pretty trying week. I do have one other thing that came up today, but it can wait."

"Good! Look at that sunset – isn't it just beautiful!"

"Absolutely!"

"What team do we play tomorrow night?"

"The Southeast Trojans! They just may give our team a run for their money. They beat us out last year by one point to win the state championship. Let's hope we'll be up for the game."

Football season was just getting cranked up. The Fair Oaks Bulldogs had won the first two games, which were out-of-conference games.

The fifteen community college athletic teams in Mississippi are divided into a North conference and a South conference. Fourteen of the fifteen schools play football. Each football team plays an out-of-conference team for the first couple of weeks each season. Then the conference play begins. The Bulldogs' game against the Trojans on Saturday will be their first conference game, against their biggest rival.

Charles & Margie went to the game, but spent much of their time visiting with colleagues from the other college, Fair Oaks faculty & staff, and fans. People like to speak to the college president, and to be honest, Caraway enjoyed mixing and mingling with colleagues and fans.

The game was an exciting one, and the Bulldogs won by three points in overtime. Their record is now 3-0 overall and 1-0 in conference play – they're off to a good start! The stands were packed for Saturday night; it was a big win for the Bulldogs!

CHAPTER FIVE

Sundays for the Caraways include an early morning breakfast of muffins; Charles almost always does the honors in the kitchen on Sunday morning. He and Margie are regulars for an 8:30 AM Sunday School couples class for older adults. They love the teacher and the intense discussions they have most Sundays. The class is active in serving needs identified at the church; the class members also gather for social events about once a month. Charles and Margie enjoy the class and the relationships that come from the association with other couples in the class. Charles is occasionally called on to sub for the teacher, but he's glad he doesn't have the responsibility as the regular teacher. He's done that off and on in other churches they have attended, and to be truthful, he's glad to be an "indian" rather than "chief" in this class.

Sunday afternoons are a time of relaxation for them for the most part. Charles particularly looked forward to this Sunday afternoon after a long week. Sometimes he spends time in his home office planning for the week, but this Sunday he opted to relax with a novel by Vince Flynn, one of his favorite authors. He would get with Judy early on Monday and map out the week. He doesn't expect a week like the last one at least, and the regular Board meeting is three weeks away.

Caraway had learned years ago that the person who thinks he doesn't have time for a good personal physical fitness program is the person who usually needs it the most. He has formed a routine over the past twenty years of getting in about thirty minutes of "cardio" exercise before anything else on Monday thru Friday. He has rarely missed a morning's workout. He has also discovered that this invigorates him; when he does miss a day, he can tell the difference. He realizes that the physical well-being of a person contributes greatly to his mental alertness, and he knows that he needs every edge he can get in his position as President. He uses the "cooling down" time just after his exercise as a devotional and daily prayer time.

After his normal routine on Monday morning, Caraway felt refreshed and ready to begin the week. He knew it had to be a better week than last week! His plan for the week included meeting with some of the administrative leadership team members to begin discussing some professional development activities that would take place in the spring. To be quite honest, he was in his element when interacting with his team about planning for the future – it energized him like nothing else could. He looked forward to this week.

Monday was an exceptionally quiet day. Caraway was able to use most of the day to catch up on email and to take care of some pending matters that were left from last week due to the extraordinary circumstances which occupied much of his time. Late Monday afternoon Caraway did spend a little quiet time thinking about whether to approach Joe Biggers about his past and, if so, how he would do that. His professional instincts said leave it alone and let the man do his job, but the side of him which always wanted to "close the loop" said get this done and put it behind him. There were pros and cons on each side. One thing in favor of just keeping the secret was that it appeared that it truly was a secret – absolutely nobody at the college knew! But what if someone did know? He left work still undecided about how to deal with the issue.

One thing for certain – no harm could come from waiting a few days if he did decide to talk with Joe.

As Charles arrived home, Margie had the pitcher of tea waiting on the deck. The weather was so nice, and the fall foliage was beginning to look like a picture.

Margie poured him a tall glass of tea.

"How was your day – did you get off to a better start for this week?"

"It was pretty much quiet and uneventful – no major problems, no repercussions from last week's problems, and no surprises."

"Good!"

Should I talk to Marge about the Joe Biggers situation? She's a good sounding board. On the other hand, why do I want to give her information about one of my very close working associates which might taint her view of him? I'm not worried about her keeping a secret - goodness knows, she's kept some pretty heavy secrets through the years. This seems so simple – I ought to be able to make up my mind about this without involving her.

Margie knew Charles well enough to see that the wheels were turning and that he was trying to decide whether to discuss something with her. She just let him alone in his solitude for a few moments. He didn't even know how much time passed while he was in such deep thought.

Finally, Margie said, "So, if there were no major problems or surprises, what did you do all day today?"

"Oh, I just did some catch-up work for what I didn't get done last week because of all the things I had going on.

Marge, can I ask you something – in a hypothetical sense?"

"Sure! You have a 'hypothetical' problem which you developed to kill some time today, since you didn't have a real one?"

"Yeah, (with a slight chuckle), I guess you could say that. Anyway, let's say you have an employee who has done something in the distant past which got them into some serious trouble, but then the record of what they did was wiped clean as a whistle. Nothing is on the books! When they applied for the job at your organization, there was a question on the application which specifically asked about the thing that the person had done - they answered that they hadn't done it. What would you do about it?"

"Well, I'd need to know some more information."

"OKay, like what?"

"Well, let's see. Have they done it again? Was it something that pertains to their job now? Are they a good employee and are they doing a good job at their current job? Do other employees know about the fact they hid the past incident? Bottom line, I guess, is does it matter now?"

There was a long silence.

"Thanks, Marge! You have a way of asking the right questions. What's for dinner?"

Charles felt a little embarrassed for having to ask Margie for guidance on this issue. She had asked the exact same questions he had, but somehow he saw the circumstances in a different light when she asked them. He now knew what he was going to do about Joe.

On Tuesday morning, Caraway buzzed Joe Biggers and asked him about a time the two of them could get together during the day. Joe said his schedule was clear after lunch until mid-afternoon, so they planned to meet in the conference room next door at 1 PM.

About mid-morning Chief Howard called on Caraway's cell phone and said he was ready to give a report on the questions Caraway had asked him to work on – could he drop by his office? Caraway was somewhat anxious about the answers, so he told the Chief to come on by.

Caraway told Judy to send the Chief in when he got there.

Chief Howard was there momentarily.

"Chief, I hope you have some good news for me."

"Well, if you ever get tired of being President, I'd make an opening for you on my force – you nailed this one!"

"Have a seat and tell me about it."

"Susie was dealing, not only in the dorm, but all over campus. She was one smooth cookie, I'll give her that. Here's how it all went down."

Chief Howard related how the officers had found the marijuana in her room the night of the drug bust. When he served the warrant on her this week, she still had evidence (out of plain view) in her room that allowed her to deliver drugs in some unique ways. One of her favorites was a zip lock plastic pen/pencil bag which she swapped at the drop each time. There were three of those in her room, all of which had traces of marijuana in them. The Chief had video of her doing several drops with those bags and was able to "turn" three people who were shown receiving the drugs to testify against her. He produced signed statements from those three.

“Dr. Caraway, can you tell me how you knew what was going on? And how did you know we’d find evidence of her dealing?”

“Just a hunch, but the first question is pretty easy. She had just 4 grams short of the amount of marijuana to be charged with a felony. Then, she went straight to a lawyer after she made bond on a misdemeanor. Think about that for just a minute.”

“Hmmm – she knew to have just under the limit for dealing - and how does she afford an attorney? And why would she make such a big deal about this if she wasn’t afraid she would get bumped up to a felony. She had less than required for an automatic felony charge, but if we have witnesses - she’s still in for the felony on dealing.”

Caraway continued, “The second question – well, we just got lucky. She was either too cocky or too dumb to get the bags out. If we’d waited just another day or so, they might have been gone.”

Chief Howard broke in, “And when we knew about the bags, we were able to put the drops together on campus with the help of our video. Like I said, if you ever need a job in law enforcement, I can give you a great reference. By the way, I’m paying some overtime to a couple of officers for all the video they had to watch!”

“Chief, let’s keep this between us. You make a file on what you did, but you take credit for the idea and everything that came after that.”

“Dr. Caraway, I have no problem with that if it’s the way you want it – we’ll keep everything as quiet as we can.“

"That's the way it needs to be. One more thing - you need to plan some regular staff development with your officers. They dropped the ball on this one – the written report on the bust that is. Let's not let that happen again."

"Yes sir. I'm already working on it."

"Oh, and just one more thing. I think you'll be hearing from Dr. Summerset regarding the issue of staff development for your officers – let it be his idea when he comes to you."

"Yes sir!"

"Have a good day, Chief!"

"You too!"

Following his conversation with Chief Howard, Caraway called Leon Burchfield on his cell phone. Burchfield answered on the second ring.

"Mr. Burchfield, have you met with Sistrunk yet?"

"Really, no, I haven't, but we're supposed to get together sometime tomorrow."

"Good! You and I need to talk before that meeting."

"What's happened? Do you have some new information?"

"As a matter of fact, I do. When and where can we meet?"

"How about the sandwich shop like before, say five o'clock?"

"That'll be fine."

Caraway and Joe Biggers met at the appointed one o'clock hour in the conference room.

"Joe, how's everything going?"

"Fine, Dr. Caraway. You know as well as I that we're really stretched for revenue right now, but 'Lord willing and the creek don't rise' we'll get through it."

Caraway asked, "How are the budget managers doing in meeting your schedule of making departmental cuts in their regular spending this fall? Do you think we're going to meet our goal for December 31?"

"Yes sir. I really think so. Everyone seems to understand the magnitude of the problem. It really helped that you spoke to the faculty and staff about this a few weeks ago in the opening faculty meetings. It also was a good call to meet with your administrative team to talk about ways to cut back. Everyone knew what we had to do, but it meant a lot that you and I actually met with them to get their ideas and suggestions. The beauty of it was that their suggestions actually identified a few things you and I hadn't thought about for making the cuts. I'm just happy at this point that we haven't had to cut any more personnel this year. The three staff members we lost last year are being missed, but we're filling in the gaps with other people, and they feel like they're making a contribution to help solve our problems."

"Good, but let me tell you how much I appreciate your handling of the details for all those things we discussed. You're doing an outstanding job!"

"Thank you, sir."

"Joe, I need to give you a heads-up on something. It is my understanding that Mr. Casco is planning to bring up the athletic building program again – maybe at the next Board meeting."

"Really? I remember when it came up several years ago. Mr. Casco seemed to be the leader then. I remember that the Board decided not to build because of a lack of funding. We sure don't have the funding now. What's he thinking?"

"Well, I'm told he may be thinking that we can spare the money from the Fund Balance."

"Are you kidding me?"

"No, Joe, I'm not kidding."

"Oh, I'm sorry, I didn't mean it that way."

"No problem. I was caught by surprise too."

"Dr. Caraway, I appreciate your giving me a heads-up, but you and the Board are the ones who'll decide this kind of thing. I only do what I'm told."

"Well, there is something I think you can do to help. We need to talk about your monthly financial report to the Board. It's a pretty comprehensive report, but we need to be prepared to discuss some things which may come up about finance."

"Dr. Caraway, you and I know that our financial system is very complicated and pretty difficult for even an accountant to understand sometimes. We're fortunate to have a few Board members who understand it well enough to ask the right questions that lead to a better understanding by everyone else. But you and I also know that we have to present it so everybody can get a picture of the bottom line. They all should know we don't have any extra money to build any facilities right now."

"I think you're right - here is what I want you to do."

Caraway explained how he wanted Joe to develop some information & charts that showed the historical picture of the college's financial position. He needed to be able to show what happened at times when there were financial "emergencies." He also needed to be prepared to discuss expenditures by classification. He asked Joe to be sure to have the breakdowns on amounts spent for athletic programs, et cetera and to think of anything else that might be helpful.

He explained to Joe that this information needed to be carefully examined before the Board meeting, but that the end result was that he needed to be particularly prepared for this Board meeting. They agreed to meet early the next week to look over the information. He also told Joe he planned to share the information with the Board chair, but he wanted to present a condensed version as a type of executive summary for the Board chair.

"By the way, Dr. Caraway, something just hit me about this athletic facility thing. A couple of months ago, Fred Baker (office accountant) & I were discussing the athletic program one day when he told me that Coach Dawson had asked him if he knew how much money the college had in the 'Reserve' fund. Fred really didn't think a lot about it, but somehow it just came out in our conversation. You know, Coach Dawson and Fred have gotten to be pretty good friends. Well, I guess I didn't think much of it at the time – people do sometimes get curious about our financial picture – do you think there could be a connection, if you know what I mean?"

"Joe, I appreciate your sharing this with me. It's probably nothing, but it does throw up a flag of sorts, doesn't it?

Well, let's just keep this between us for now. I wouldn't want to go off half-cocked on a possible connection."

"Yes sir, you got it. I'll put some things together on the information and charts, et cetera. It'll be easy enough, and I'll have some files in my brief case at the Board meeting which contain this information."

"Good. Thanks, Joe."

When Caraway and Burchfield met later that afternoon, Caraway wasted no time in providing him a copy of the written report he had received from Chief Howard. When Burchfield had had time to read the report, Caraway took over the conversation.

"Susie was dealing drugs at my college. According to video we have, we think she's been doing it for at least six months. When we happened to get lucky through an informant and find marijuana in her room, she immediately pulled out the big guns to try and scare us into dropping the whole thing. Of course, our bungling of the appeals process played right into her hands. Things looked pretty one sided there for a while.

We've got enough to get her convicted on a felony charge that would land her in prison for probably three to five years, if we decide to press this thing all the way. So, here's the deal. We will not press the DA on this – yes, I know we're obligated to turn over the information we have, but we won't press for the maximum. She's out of the dorm and out of our school. She signs a statement that you draw up dropping all charges in exchange for our not pushing the case against her. That's the deal. What do you think?"

"First, remind me never to get on your bad side. "

"I'm just trying to take care of my college, particularly the students. You realize how many students she may have corrupted over the past six months? I'm not inclined to cut her any slack."

"I can see that. I'd say you've done your homework pretty well – and your Chief has done a great job of putting all this together."

"Yes he did – and I'm grateful for a way out of this."

"I assume you want me to meet with Mr. Sistrunk and deliver the news and make the deal. I'll need to meet with Cecil Hatfield over in the DA's office as well. They need to know our position on this."

"Of course. But I want something else from you."

"What's that?"

"Attorney client privilege."

"That's pretty much a given."

"Well, yes, but as you and I have discussed before, you represent the Board, not me personally. I don't want this news to get out any more than absolutely necessary."

"You mean, you want to keep it from the Board?"

"No, I plan to discuss it confidentially with the Board chair; he can take it from there, but for obvious reasons I'd like to keep this as confidential as possible."

"No problem."

"Good. Call me on my cell when you've met with Sistrunk. If he don't take the deal, tell him we'll see him in court."

"Somehow, I don't think that will be a problem. This seems to be a no-brainer!"

CHAPTER SJX

On Wednesday morning Summerset and Berryman showed up for their appointment at nine o'clock sharp. They'd taken their assignment seriously and had produced several typewritten pages that covered procedures for due process issues. They pointed out some things they did wrong, or more to the point, some things they didn't do; they made it clear that no adverse action would be taken against a student again until due process had been provided to that student. In addition to the assignment, they had already contacted Chief Howard and local law enforcement and fire department officials to begin developing a plan for dealing with several types of emergencies, such as evacuation, lock down, et cetera.

Summerset indicated that he had directed Chief Howard to plan some staff development for his officers – they could have done a much better job. Procedure was okay, but the record keeping and reporting were way short.

Caraway spent the rest of the day Wednesday in a meeting with three members of his administrative team, Dr. John Ford, his VP for Instruction, Dr. Melanie Sutton, Academic Dean, and Dr. Agnes Dupree, Dean of Career-Technical Instruction.

John Ford had worked his way up through the ranks in Britton Community College, another community college district within the state, where he had twelve years' administrative experience as an academic dean and had been at Fair Oaks for the past fourteen years as VP of Instruction. He was a very valuable asset to Caraway, not only in the instructional arena where he worked, but as a confidant and "sounding board" who knew the ropes. More importantly, he was one in whom Caraway could place his trust without question.

Melanie Sutton had been at Fair Oaks for eighteen years, first as an instructor in the Mathematics Division for ten years, and then as Dean of Academic Instruction for the past eight years. She was known for her instructional integrity and had a reputation for fairness, but was also a stickler for following the rules. It was no wonder that she had developed a great rapport with faculty and staff. She provided sound oversight of the academic program at the college. She had chaired the statewide association of academic deans and was respected in the community college system around the state as one of the best deans ever to hold office.

Agnes Dupree began work at the college twenty-two years ago as an instructor in the Medical Laboratory Technician (MLT) program, went back to college to earn her Bachelor's Degree in Allied Science Education, and then her Master's and Doctorate Degrees in Educational Administration. She has served as Dean for the past six years.

Caraway encouraged his administrative leaders to think "out of the box" and to try things which had not necessarily been tried before. He liked to listen to their ideas and plans for program enrichment for faculty and staff. Today's meeting was mostly about how to provide new opportunities for administrative staff enrichment for the coming year.

Caraway remembered that last year the team had placed a priority on faculty enrichment, and following that session they had put in place a project called "Taping for Improvement" an instructional video-taping program whereby classroom instructors were given the opportunity to have their classes video-taped by a student who'd been trained for the task. At the end of class the student removed the tape from the camera and handed it to the instructor as he/she left the room. The instructor then had the opportunity to watch the video of the class in private on his/her own time to self-evaluate the class meeting. It was so simple; once the trust factor was gotten across to faculty that it truly was their private viewing of the tape that was important, it had really caught on.

Just one year later, over twenty-five percent of the instructors had participated in the project. The best part was that almost all who had participated had given it raving reviews. In reality, future participation was probably going to be limited by the amount of equipment available for taping. The head librarian had submitted a budget request for additional equipment for the coming year to allow for the project's growth, but Caraway was keenly aware that the budget crunch could stall the natural growth of this great project. In light of the reviews and the requests by additional faculty to participate, he had to put a priority on finding at least some money to buy additional equipment.

As they discussed plans for the administrative staff development, Caraway and the others were keenly aware of the critical role played by mid-level administrative personnel, so today's meeting was about discussing new ways to provide opportunities for administrative personnel to grow professionally. As they began the meeting Caraway mentioned that there were several publications out that dealt with leadership that he wanted administrative personnel to read and discuss. Of course, the list included The 7 Habits of Highly Effective People and other books by Steven Covey and some recent publications by other authors as well. A new book that Caraway particularly wanted to consider using was Tony Dungy's The Mentor Leader. He also suggested they use one of his favorites, Good to Great, by Jim Collins. Both of these books would be great tools for moving the administrative team forward.

Advance reading would be required, so materials would need to be ordered. The group discussed how to use the books most effectively to promote not only good decision-making, but also "mentor-leader" relationships that would strengthen those who could provide leadership as well as those who needed a mentor.

Caraway had been a supporter of the newly formed statewide leadership academy for community college personnel. The academy was sponsored by the MS Community College Foundation (MCCF), and since a major state university had been a partner since the beginning, participants were able to receive graduate credit at the university toward a masters or doctorate degree in Ed Leadership for the work completed in the academy.

Each of the fifteen community colleges had been invited to place two people in the academy each year, but Caraway planned to ask for a third position this year. Those who had attended in previous years had matured in their leadership skills, but also had developed a whole new concept of what leadership was about. He planned to use their expertise in future leadership development at Fair Oaks. Both Dr. Sutton and Dr. Dupree were graduates of the Academy.

As usual, Caraway felt good about the progress made by the end of the planning session. He finished off the day with routine office work, including his late afternoon check on email and messages received during the day.

By Thursday morning three Board members had called Caraway to let him know they had been contacted by John Casco asking them to support a motion to build the athletic complex. They wanted to know if Dr. Caraway was aware of these contacts by Mr. Casco and whether there was money for this project. He told each one that he appreciated the call – and that, although Mr. Casco hadn't discussed this with him, he was aware there had been some contacts and that he wasn't sure how Mr. Casco planned to pay for the project. When the Board members had asked for his opinion, he had very calmly explained that he didn't see how they could spend such an amount of money in the near future, but that he was certainly open to listen to ideas if anyone had any.

One notable call was from Miss Eleanor Montrose. Miss Montrose, a retired school teacher who had served on the Board for sixteen years, had been appointed the year after her retirement as an elementary teacher from the local school system. No one knew how old she was and wouldn't dare ask, but she must be on the back side of seventy years. She had never married and had devoted her entire life to education, first as a teacher and now as a Board member. Caraway mentally noted that her age did not slow her down a bit!

Caraway was impressed with the people who served on his Board of Trustees. Miss Montrose was just one example of a Board member who put their heart and soul into trying to make good decisions for the college so individuals from all walks of life could take advantage of a rock solid education that was accessible and affordable. Other Board members represented the medical profession, bankers & lawyers, but most members of the Board were just regular business men & women. Caraway was proud to see a few retired educators like Miss Montrose on the Board as well. All in all, he was very pleased with a great representation of a cross section of the community and with the wisdom those people brought with them to the Board.

Notwithstanding the calls about the drum-beating by Mr. Casco, the week was going pretty well until Thursday about mid-afternoon when Judy buzzed Caraway.

“Dr. Caraway, Barry Smith is on the line and wishes to come by this afternoon to discuss a matter with you.”

“I’m right in the middle of writing a major part of my speech for Rotary. Would you see if he can wait ‘til in the morning?”

“Yes sir, I’ll check.”

“Sir, he says it is not urgent, but that it is rather sensitive and that you would want to know what he has to tell you.”

“Well, it’s almost 4 o’clock. Tell him I’ll see him at 5 o’clock. When you leave, please leave the door where he can get in. “

“Sir, he has a key, so why don’t I just lock the door so you won’t be disturbed for a while.”

“Good idea – tell him to let himself in at five o’clock. I’ll see you in the morning, Judy, have a good night.”

“You too, sir.”

Caraway was conscious of the fact that Barry reported to Dr. Ford, but he made it a personal policy to be accessible to members of the faculty or staff when requested. He knew how to steer them in the right direction if that was needed.

Caraway made a mental note to work on the speech early the next week. He had 'til Thursday of that week to get it ready. He would just need to put the finishing touches on it next week.

When Barry arrived at five o'clock sharp, he knocked before entering. Somehow he didn't feel comfortable just walking into the President's office.

"Come in, Barry."

"Sir, I appreciate your seeing me this afternoon. I just have an issue I need get your advice on that's rather sensitive."

"What's the problem, Barry?"

"Dr. Caraway, you're somewhat familiar with technology and electronics in general, so you'll understand what I'm about to say to some extent. "

"Barry, I just know enough to get by, but go ahead."

"Well, sir, we have a filter in place for the entire college that doesn't allow inappropriate information, etc. into the servers. That system has a recording feature that only a very few people are aware of, pretty much just a couple of staff members who have to know."

"Okay. I'm aware that the college made the decision several years ago to filter out certain types of spam, certainly pornography and other types of offensive material. I'm familiar with that."

"Yes, sir, I know you are. But what you probably don't know is that we make a record on one of the servers of ANY and ALL of that type material that DOES come through."

"But, I thought you said it can't come through!"

"Yes sir, for the most part, that's true. However, there are always some exceptions."

"What kind of exceptions?"

"Sir, any screen, firewall, filter, or whatever you call it can be hacked through if the person knows how."

"So, you're saying we are vulnerable to 'hackers' if they're good enough – I guess I'm really not that surprised, but why are we having this conversation?"

"Sir, we have a hacker that's getting 'inappropriate' information into our system. He's downloaded, probably onto a flash drive, over a hundred pictures of sexually explicit material through a computer in our network."

"So, exactly how do you know this?"

"The recording device is one of those things which requires lots of memory, so we have to transfer it to a disk every 3 months. We don't normally look at material that's come through unless we have reason, but occasionally we scan a certain file that gives us an idea of any type of material that's not quite right."

"Okay, Barry, give me the bad news. I see it coming."

"Sir, Thomas Mitchell (a full-time English instructor at Fair Oaks) has been downloading pornography off and on for about six months now. That's as far back as we can determine, but there could be more. We just know of the past six months."

"Mr. Mitchell?"

"Yes sir."

"So, you discovered this by looking at what had come through, and when you found something, you went back how far?"

"A year, sir."

"I'm shocked," Caraway responded, almost to himself, "Tom's a family man, and I know he's probably not the most conservative person socially, but this is really a shock. I know he's one heck of a classroom instructor."

"Sir, you can see why I need your advice – actually direction, because this is not my call. You need to tell me what to do."

"Barry, for now, I want you to do two things. First, do not discuss this with anyone. I assume you haven't already done so."

"That's correct, sir – you and I are the only two people who know about this."

"Let's keep it that way for now. The second thing is I want you to personally take care of the review of material you mentioned and make a personal log of when you see it coming through the system.

Actually, I need to ask you an important question, and I want you to think about it carefully before answering it. Did you seen anything that looked like "child pornography when you were reviewing the material?"

"Sir?"

"Barry, you may not be aware that 'child pornography' constitutes a much greater problem for Mr. Mitchell – and for us. If there is anything that falls into that category, we are obliged to report it to the authorities. So, again, do you recall anything that looks like it could fall into that category?"

"Sir, I have to tell you that I haven't looked too closely – it really is repulsive to me."

"Do you feel like you can go back and get a handle on that question? If it's not pretty obvious I wouldn't worry too much."

"Yes sir. I'll take a look, but......"

"But what?"

"Sir, what if someone sees me reviewing this stuff? I can't take it home, and you know my staff has to work at all hours. Someone could drop in on me at any time."

"Barry, I appreciate your concern. How much time do you think this stuff will take to review?"

"Probably not too long - I think I can handle it ok. I'll come in over the weekend and take a look. "

"Good. Let me know if you have any problems. I need to know if anyone else knows about this. And I especially need to know if you find any child porn. While you're looking, I think we'd be prudent to take a quick look at Mr. Mitchell's email for say the last two months. I assume you can do that."

"Yes sir, but what are we looking for in the email?"

"I don't know. I just know that people do some strange things on email, so let's take a quick look. We've got justification after what you've already found."

"Yes sir. I plan to work late tonight and/or Friday and Saturday nights and get this over with."

"Good! Good night Barry."

"Good night, Dr. Caraway."

Caraway made himself a note to talk with John Ford, who had supervisory responsibility for computer technology, the next morning to bring him up-to-date on this situation. He finished up in the office and took a copy of his speech home to review. He always liked to read over his notes and become familiar with them. Then when he gave the actual speech, he left the notes in his folder and just talked about the major points in his own words. He had heard too many people read from their notes when speaking to a group; he was determined not to do that, and he had plenty of time to review the notes, since his speech was a week away.

CHAPTER SEVEN

On Friday morning, earlier than normal lawyer's hours, Leon Burchfield called Caraway with the news from Mr. Sistrunk.

"Dr. Caraway, I thought I'd give you the good news early on Friday to make your day and close out the week on a good note!"

"Good. I assume Mr. Sistrunk went for the deal on behalf of Susie."

"Oh yeah! I think he was as surprised as any attorney I have ever seen about his client. She'd really fed him a line, and he must have been looking for a reason to file a complaint against the college. He evidently didn't do much research on this case – it must have looked like an easy way to make a buck. Don't know what Susie was going to pay, but she probably was ok financially, given the last four months."

"How about the DA's office? "

Burchfield related that Cecil Hatfield, Assistant DA, had already talked with Susie and that a plea bargain was in the works.

"This may wind up being a big bust for the locals. It looks like Susie's making a deal to "turn" her supplier – they think he's the number two guy in this part of the state. Anyway, they mentioned the idea of putting Susie back in play with a wire to try to get the big guy. They're willing to reduce her time to probably 18 months, instead of 3-5 years."

"As long as they don't involve the college – we don't need any publicity on this."

"I understand, and I've communicated that to them very clearly. She does not set foot back on campus. They've got to find another venue."

"Good! Well, Mr. Burchfield, you did make my day. I appreciate your help on this matter. By the way, I have another situation which may require your services, but I hope not. I'll let you know."

"Dr. Caraway, I need to tell you - I enjoy working with people who give me a heads-up on things which may become a legal matter, rather than call me to tell me 'we're in big trouble'! Just keep that in mind. You did well on this other matter. Keep up the good work. Let me know if you need me."

"Thanks – I really hope I won't need to call you. Oh, I almost forgot – I guess you could call this a 'heads-up' – there may be some issues which will need some careful guidance at the next Board meeting – bring your 'parliamentary procedures hat' with you just in case."

"Thanks – you want to tell me what this involves?"

"Let's have coffee one day next week and I'll fill you in. It's not urgent, and things may change, so let's wait."

"Good by me."

As he hung up the phone with the Board attorney, Caraway was thinking this conversation pretty much closed out the chapter on the Susie Jones affair. Hopefully, that would be the end of it. He headed home for the day and for the weekend. He looked forward to the weekends more these days.

The weather on Saturday morning was absolutely perfect for golf. Caraway enjoyed playing eighteen holes with his friend who was passing through on his way south. They played on a nearby course and had lunch at the grill in the pro shop. Caraway's round wasn't great, with a score of ninety-two, but he rationalized that it had been several months since he'd played. His friend did slightly better with an eighty-six. The bottom line for both of them was that they'd enjoyed playing and visiting with each other that morning. Caraway promised himself he was going to get out more often.

That afternoon Charles & Margie travelled to Boxley, a small town in south Mississippi, for the football game against the Twin Rivers Bears; they broke bread with his friend and colleague, Everett Parker, President of Twin Rivers, before the game. There was a long-lasting tradition in Mississippi community college football that the hosting college president would invite the president from the visiting team to enjoy a meal together before game time. Charles and Margie had looked forward to visiting with Everett & his wife Carole on a casual basis on this occasion.

The Bears had been a fairly weak team in recent years, but you never knew in the community college league in Mississippi - there had been some pretty big upsets in years past. Caraway was sure the coaches had prepared the players for the possibility that the Bears would probably be tougher than the scouting report showed.

Dr. Everett Parker was one of the senior members of the Presidents' Association, having been at Twin Rivers for some thirty-two years and president for the past fourteen years. Although Caraway had known him for a short two years, he already considered him to be a close friend, as well as one to look to for guidance in the Presidents' Association. He knew the Mississippi community college system like a book and had a lot of wisdom to share with other presidents on the finer points of how to run a community college. In addition to his wisdom regarding community colleges, Everett had a long lasting friendship with several key legislators and knew his way around the Capitol – that was very valuable to the Presidents' Association, especially when their bills were being considered.

The game against the Bears went somewhat as expected. The final score was 31 to 10, but the game was actually much closer than the score indicated. Caraway thought the Bulldogs played well, but certainly not to what he thought was their potential. He hoped they would play better in future games when opponents would likely be a lot tougher.

Caraway saw several of his Board members at the game, including John Casco. He and Casco spoke briefly during half time while in the concession line. Casco was very cordial in the short meeting of the two men, and no mention was made by either of them about the upcoming effort to build facilities on the home side of the stadium. Caraway was actually relieved because he didn't want to discuss this subject with John just yet, especially in public at a ballgame.

Once again Charles opted not to work in his home office over the weekend to plan for the next week. Margie suggested they spend Sunday afternoon visiting with their son Adam and family some one hundred miles away in north Mississippi. Since Adam was an only child, that made it very special to visit with him. He and his wife Norma had two sons, Todd, eleven and Timmy, nine years of age. One of the reasons Charles and Margie had moved back to Mississippi was to be closer to their son and his family. Charles was blessed that the president's position at Fair Oaks had become open about the time he was looking to move back to Mississippi. Life was good for the Caraways!

Charles got an early start on Monday. As usual after a weekend, he was rejuvenated and ready for the new challenges of the week. He wondered how it had gone with Barry Smith and the review he was going to do over the weekend. He thought he'd give Barry until afternoon to call him to let him know what he found. He was somewhat worried that there could be a need to contact the local authorities about the problem. If he had to get them involved, they would take control of the situation to a large extent – he did not want that to happen because it would seriously limit how he dealt with a personnel issue at his college.

After lunch Barry called and asked if he could come by to discuss the matter with Caraway. Caraway asked if he could just give him a report over the phone. Barry indicated that things were somewhat different than he expected and that they should talk face to face.

"Okay, give me fifteen minutes and then let Judy know when you're here."

Now what! Caraway had no idea what Barry meant by things being "somewhat different" than he expected. Either he'd found the "kiddy porn" or he hadn't.

Caraway returned two short calls and got those off his list of things to do before Barry got there.

"Dr. Caraway, Barry Smith is here to see you."

"Send him in. And Judy, would you ask Dr. Ford to join us and then make sure we're not disturbed."

"Yes sir."

Within just a few moments Dr. Ford joined them.

Caraway began, "Okay, Barry. Let's have it. What have you found now?"

"Dr. Caraway, we have a whole different problem now."

Caraway felt like Barry had just sucker punched him in the stomach, again!

"Okay. What've you got?"

"Well, when I was looking through Mr. Mitchell's email, I found some pretty kinky emails between him and someone who calls herself Wendy."

"Do you have a last name for Wendy?"

"Sir, I didn't try to actually identify her – the IP address was actually one in a computer lab over in Sutter Hall, so I didn't try to ID her. I can tell you which computer, actually three different computers, she used, but I really don't know if that's even her real name."

"Do you know if she's a student at Fair Oaks?"

"No sir, not really, but it appears she might be."

"Okay. Tell me about the email."

"Cybersex, sir."

"Alright – tell me for sure that this is Tom Mitchell. Could anyone else be doing this on his computer? I assume he was not stupid enough to use his real name on the emails."

"The name on the email was TIM, all caps."

"TIM? Did you check to see if that's his initials?"

"Yes sir. His middle name is Ivan."

"Okay, back to my question. How sure are you that Mr. Mitchell's the one who's doing this?"

"Sir, I'm ninety-nine percent sure that it's being done from his computer, but...."

"You're ninety-nine percent sure? Either it's his computer or it's not."

"Sir, there's a 'remote' chance; actually that word is rather appropriately used here with a double meaning. There's a chance that someone is just using Mr. Mitchell's computer as a drone – they could be getting in by "remote" from ...well, from anywhere."

"You give that about one percent chance?"

"Sir, have you heard the expression, 'there ain't no horse that can't be rode, and there ain't no cowboy that can't be throwed'?"

Both Caraway and Ford laughed. Caraway replied, "It's been a while since I heard that one. How does it apply to this situation?"

"Most anything in the world of technology can be done. I'm just saying that there's a very 'remote' chance that someone, from somewhere – maybe China for all I know, for some reason, could be getting into Mr. Mitchell's computer. I personally doubt it, but I cannot rule it out."

"Okay, how do we find out for sure?"

"Dr. Caraway, that'll take a lot longer than this assignment did, and I might need some help."

"Help? From whom?"

"Well, one of my tech guys could be a lot of help – it's really going to take some time."

"Barry, I'm sorry – we can't do that. I don't want anyone else to know – do you realize a person's reputation and maybe his livelihood is at stake here? How much time will you need?"

"By myself, probably a good week. Do you really think that kind of time is necessary? I mean, it's such a slight chance it's not Mr. Mitchell."

Caraway just looked at Barry with no displayed emotion as if to say *what did I just say?*

Barry caught on, "Okay, okay. I got the picture, but it really could take some serious time."

"Barry, when we approach Mr. Mitchell, we've got to know he's the guilty party. We could talk to him about this and perhaps get his confession, but what if he's not the guy? Think of the repercussions. First, he would lose confidence in the administration, the institution, and everyone else. We just can't go off half cocked in accusing someone of this type thing. Second, the word would get out – there goes the confidence factor again, multiplied by a hundred. And third, he might be upset enough to bring some type of legal action against the college. No - we have to know beyond a doubt if that's at all possible."

"Yes sir. I understand. I just want to be sure we're not wasting so much time in light of the minute chance is not him."

"Barry, let's rule out the one percent factor."

"Yes sir."

"And Barry, we need to know who Wendy is – if she's a student, we've got a bigger problem. Let me know – you said about a week?"

"Yes sir."

"Okay, I'll hold off on doing anything 'til I hear from you. Let me know if you need anything, and be careful – you need to find a reason for all the late night hours. Is your wife going to understand this?"

"She'll be okay, sir. I sometimes run into some heavy duty situations with the network that mean I have to spend late night hours at the shop."

"Good. Okay. I'll expect to hear back from you by next Monday. Let me know if that time frame changes, and be careful."

"Yes sir."

John Ford had sat quietly while Caraway talked with Barry. He was already accustomed, in a short twenty-four months, to sitting in on conversations between the President and others. It actually saved Caraway the time & effort of explanation about the conversation; Ford knew Caraway would expect his opinion on the matter after the meeting.

As Barry left his office Caraway asked John what he thought. He knew Ford would give him an honest straight forward "no holds barred" answer.

"Well, I would probably have called Tom Mitchell in and asked him, saved Barry a week of work. But ...., I see your point. I assume you'll want me to be the one to talk with Mitchell first when the time comes."

"I think we just might talk with him together, but let's see how this plays out."

The two of them called it a day and headed home.

CHAPTER EIGHT

Caraway was out on campus by 6:45 on Tuesday morning. He loved the early morning hours, and after his morning exercise and quiet time he often started the day having coffee and visiting with the maintenance staff. Like every community college president, he's expected to know everything that's going on at Fair Oaks – that, of course, isn't possible, but he'd found that he learned a lot about what's happening on campus during those early morning visits. Some staff person usually wanted to show him something that was wrong or something that was new. He had quickly learned in his tenure as president how much he could learn about campus life on these early morning visits, and the maintenance staff appreciated him taking an interest in what they did.

When he left the maintenance facility he spent the next couple of hours making the rounds to several faculty office suites, just visiting. He didn't get to do that very often, so he especially enjoyed the interaction among faculty and support staff when he did. They too appreciated his showing up for those unannounced visits. When he was dean, in a former life, he was able to spend much more time mingling with the faculty and staff, but the president's office wasn't quite the same.

Caraway got to his office just past mid-morning.

"Good morning, Judy, any calls I need to return this morning? "

"Yes sir" – she handed him a stack of phone messages, some of which required a return call. That would occupy a major portion of his morning.

Down the hall John Ford was having a meeting with Dr. Melanie Sutton and Mr. George Jacobson, Political Science Instructor. Leading up to this meeting there had been other meetings with Mr. Jacobson, first with Thomas Butler, Division Chair for Social Science, and then with Dr. Sutton.

Mr. Jacobson has taught American National Government at Fair Oaks for the past thirty years and has been there longer than all but two other instructors. The annual student evaluations for his classroom performance have always been a little above average. He had stayed below the radar until last spring, when Mr. Butler had met with him regarding student complaints that he had been embarrassing athletes and cheerleaders in class.

Students had complained that Jacobson purposefully embarrassed the popular students who participated in intercollegiate activities. When they finally complained to Mr. Butler, he'd investigated and found that when the star quarterback for the football team had not known the answer to a question, Jacobson had said, "Instead of spending your time on the football field, maybe you should consider opening the book for this class sometime?"

In Butler's meeting with Jacobson in the spring of the year, the instructor had responded that, "I may have said something like that."

Butler continued, "It was also reported that you told a cheerleader, 'I doubt seriously that you know the language this text is written in, well it's English; instead of spending all your time in cheerleader practice, maybe you should try reading it sometime; it's really not that hard, probably eighth grade level.' What is your response to that, Mr. Jacobson? "

"I think I may have been misquoted, but the fact is she hadn't cracked the book one time during the semester!"

Butler followed with, "Don't you think that's a little too harsh, besides the fact that it appears that you're singling out athletes and cheerleaders?"

"Perhaps, but I've obviously gotten their attention, and yours!"

"This really isn't the kind of attention you need, and this practice needs to stop!"

"I was just trying to impress on my students that it's important that students be prepared for class, even if they are 'popular' students on campus!"

Mr. Butler just looked at him and said, "Mr. Jacobson..."

"Okay, I see your point. I'll be more careful henceforth."

Mr. Butler had taken time to write the incident up for his file and had put a copy of a memo to Mr. Jacobson in the personnel file.

No more than a month after this incident Mr. Butler was made aware of more complaints of a similar nature. He confronted Mr. Jacobson with these new complaints and once again admonished him. And, once again, Jacobson agreed to stop. Butler thought this would surely be the last of this type complaint against Mr. Jacobson. He simply added a note in the personnel file and thought no more of it.

It was about the second week of September when Dean Sutton had received more complaints about Mr.

Jacobson's class. This time the nature of the complaints was that he was spending almost all of the class time in American Government talking about politics and what was happening in "liberal" Washington, D.C. After one student had been browbeaten and embarrassed for asking Mr. Jacobson to spend more time on the subject matter, other students had been very reluctant to complain. Finally, several students had gone to see Dean Sutton.

Dr. Sutton had listened to the student complaints and had then met with Mr. Butler, who had reminded her that Mr. Jacobson had been cited for student complaints last spring, on two different occasions. Both had concluded that Jacobson's behavior was very unusual in both of these instances. Maybe he had something going on in his personal life that he was bringing to work with him. Dr. Sutton told Mr. Butler she would handle the most recent situation.

Dr. Sutton met with Mr. Jacobson to discuss the complaints. In that meeting, which she recorded in accordance with standard procedure, Mr. Jacobson became very defensive and belligerent, saying that he had a right under the principle of "academic freedom" to talk about most anything he wanted as long as it even "remotely" related to what he was teaching. Dr. Sutton relented that yes, he had a great deal of latitude under the principle of academic freedom, but that he had been hired to teach American National Government, and it appeared that he wasn't doing that because he was spending too much time on other areas of discussion.

After a fairly lengthy discussion, Dr. Sutton could see that she was getting nowhere with Jacobson, and when he had argued that he, not she, could best define what "government" was, she had lost patience with him; she looked him squarely in the eye and said, "Mr. Jacobson, you listen to me. It's your responsibility to teach the subject for which you have been employed. It's my responsibility to make sure that you're doing that. It is my conclusion, given the number and nature of student complaints and this conversation, that you are not doing that. And unless I have your commitment that you'll get back on track to teach what you're paid to teach, I will recommend to Dr. Ford that you be removed from the classroom. Is that clear?"

"Yes, it's quite clear. Now, you listen to me. I don't agree with your decision, so I'll appeal your decision to Dr. Ford, and then to the President if I have to do so! Is that clear?"

Dr. Sutton had been willing to give him another chance, but when he didn't agree to stop the practice, she knew she had to bump this to the next level.

"Perfectly, Mr. Jacobson. I'll write the necessary letters to you and to Dr. Ford today. When you get my letter, you'll need to contact Dr. Ford in writing within three working days to notify him of your appeal. I'm sure he'll schedule a hearing for you as soon as possible. It'll certainly be within three work days of his receiving notice of your intent to appeal. You are to continue your duties until this matter is resolved, but I strongly recommend you get back to the 'principles of government.'"

The meeting ended rather abruptly. After Sutton's terse response to Jacobson's tirade, it was as if time stood still - both Jacobson and Sutton just looked at each other for a full moment. They each knew the meeting had gotten out of hand. Jacobson left without another word.

Following the meeting, Sutton had written to Jacobson advising him of her recommendation and had also written the letter to Dr. Ford recommending Mr. Jacobson's removal from the classroom, in essence termination, since he had no other services to offer the college. She and Dr. Ford had discussed the matter and had decided that the appeal should be sooner rather than later. Jacobson's appeal to Dr. Ford was scheduled for today and was now being conducted in Dr. Ford's office.

Dr. Ford began the meeting, "Mr. Jacobson, thank you for meeting with us today. Just so we have an accurate record of this meeting, I'm going to tape this conversation. Do you have any objection to that?"

"Of course not. May I have a copy of the tape?"

"Yes, you may."

Dr. Ford stated the date, time and place of the meeting and indicated those who were present. He also stated that the purpose of this meeting was to hear Mr. Jacobson's "side of the story" regarding his using class time to discuss issues other than principles of American government. Ford stated for the record that Dr. Sutton was in attendance in case there was a question of fact that she needed to confirm.

He began the meeting by asking Mr. Jacobson if the facts stated in Dr. Sutton's letter of recommendation were accurate. Instead of answering the question, Jacobson said, "I've been doing some reading up on academic freedom, and I believe it guarantees me the right to use whatever means I choose to provide a good education to my classes in the area of government."

"Mr. Jacobson, let's be sure we're talking about the same set of facts before we get to explanations, so please answer my question as to whether you have differences you wish to discuss regarding Dr. Sutton's facts as reported in her letter of recommendation to me."

Jacobson answered, "yes, well, for the record, I don't disagree with the actual facts as reported by Dr. Sutton. But I do disagree with the interpretation that has been made of those facts. It is my place to determine what constitutes 'government' for my class, not Dr. Sutton. It's my right to decide how I'll teach my students! That right is protected by what is known as 'academic freedom!'"

Ford responded, "I don't know what you've been reading, Mr. Jacobson, but I think you have a mistaken view of 'academic freedom.' It may allow you to talk about political races and politics in general as a part of your subject matter; however, you are still under contract to teach the course *American National Government,* not a comparative politics course such as you seem to be doing!"

"I simply disagree! I feel that I have the right to 'academic freedom' in my classroom! Government involves politics!"

"Mr. Jacobson, it seems we have reached an impasse here. You have certain rights to teach your classes within the scope of the subject matter for those classes. As a matter of fact you have great latitude to do so. However, the college administration has a right, even a duty, to protect the academic integrity of all courses. I might add that we have accountability not only to our constituents, but also to the accreditation agencies which oversee the academic integrity of institutions in the region. There are parameters to which we all must adhere, and you have crossed the line in not adhering to those parameters. You've been teaching government at Fair Oaks for the past thirty years and we've never had an issue with your straying from the subject in the past. What's changed?"

"Well, Dr. Ford, in case you haven't noticed, the 'liberals' have taken control of our government in Washington. They have strayed away from, no they've totally disregarded, the U.S. Constitution, and it's my responsibility to point out the problem to our students!"

"With all due respect, Mr. Jacobson, no matter how noble you feel the cause, that is not your responsibility. Your responsibility is to teach the principles of government.

So, now you have a choice to decide whether you will comply with the direction by Dr. Sutton and me to teach the subject matter for which you have been employed. If you cannot do that, then I will have no choice but to recommend that your employment as an instructor at Fair Oaks be terminated immediately."

"In other words you're firing me because I choose to teach my classes in a certain way. Is that it?"

"Mr. Jacobson, we are recording this conversation. I stated what our expectations are, and, once again, you have the choice of whether you will comply with those expectations of employment."

"I know you are recording this meeting – you told me that! What I don't understand is why I can't teach my classes as I wish. Once again, 'academic freedom' gives me the right to do that!"

"Mr. Jacobson, we are getting nowhere. I have no choice but to recommend your termination as a classroom instructor at Fair Oaks. I will put my decision in writing to you, and will also advise you in writing that you have the right to appeal this decision in writing to President

Caraway within three days of your receipt of my written notice. You will return to your classes until this matter is concluded through the appeals process, but you will cease and desist forthwith from using class time to discuss anything beyond the subject matter for your course."

"When can I see the President? Is he available today – I'd like to get this settled."

"You will have to check with his office and set an appointment. He will receive a copy of my letter to you by this time tomorrow. I'm sure he'll hear your appeal as soon as possible; however, I'm sure he'll want to get all the facts before he meets with you."

"Oh, I'll give him the facts alright! Dr. Sutton and Mr. Butler have been trying to set me up to be fired for the past several months."

"Mr. Jacobson, can you share with me anything that substantiates that accusation?"

"I could, but I see that you're in it with them so I think I'll wait and share that with President Caraway."

Mr. Jacobson had a very belligerent attitude and was being very uncooperative; John Ford's patience had reached the limit with him. "The record will show that this conference is concluded. When you get my letter, advise Dr. Caraway's office that you wish to appeal."

After the conference, Ford and Sutton decided that Dr. Caraway needed to be advised about this situation immediately. Ford had actually given Dr. Caraway a "heads-up" after he got Dr. Sutton's report of her meeting with Mr. Jacobson. He related to Caraway that he was not overly optimistic that the situation would be resolved without a dismissal.

Ford buzzed Judy and asked that he and Dr. Sutton be put on Dr. Caraway's schedule at the earliest possible time.

Caraway had returned several of his calls and had then settled down to work on other routine matters that Judy had left on his desk earlier in the morning. He called Joe Biggers to get a status report on the work he was doing in preparation for the Board meeting.

"Joe, how are you doing on the information for the Board meeting?"

"It's going pretty well – I have some people working on the charts and figures that kind of compare expenses. It really is pretty routine, so I decided it would be better to let it be a natural thing by having it done as a matter of course. "

"Joe, I need to make sure you have one other item covered in your information for the Board meeting. A question may be raised about the money that's been spent on the health occupations programs a few years ago – there may be some comparison to athletics. We need to look closely at the expenses for those programs and be able to show job placement for completers in those programs. I just have a hunch this could become an issue."

"No problem. I don't know what the facts will reveal exactly, although I think the decision was a wise one, but I can get the facts for you. I'm sure Dr. Dupree already *has* the facts – we just need to put them into some form that presents a clear picture."

"Good. Get Dr. Dupree to assist you in putting this together."

"Of course."

"Good. I think it best that we keep the rationale for this report to ourselves for now. I don't want to put any undue pressure on Dr. Dupree just now."

"I agree, sir."

"Good. How long to get that together? "

"Probably a couple of days, maybe before the end of the day tomorrow, depending on what Dr. Dupree has on file already and how soon we can get together."

"Good. Thanks! If you need my help, let me know. And oh, just so you know, I'll bring Dr. Ford up to speed on this later in the day. You can work with him as needed on this project."

"Yes sir."

As soon as Caraway was off the phone with Joe, Judy buzzed him and indicated Dr. Ford had called and wanted to know if he and Dr. Sutton could meet with him on an important matter. Caraway asked her to have them come on down to his office.

Caraway had a great working relationship with Drs. Ford and Sutton. He had had a very frank conversation with several of his leadership team shortly after he came to Fair Oaks as President about the fact that a college president had a great need to have at least a few people that he could have complete confidence in to "tell him like it is." John Ford and Melanie Sutton were two of those people.

Ford opened the meeting, “Good morning Dr. Caraway. We just need to give you a heads-up on a matter that’s coming your way.“

“Dr. Ford, I need to update you on a couple of matters as well. You and Dr. Sutton go first.”

“Dr. Sutton has had some complaints that Mr. Jacobson has been spending a large portion of his time in his government class talking about politics instead of teaching the principles of government.”

“That sounds like a problem Dr. Sutton could handle without you or me. There must be more to it than that!”

“Yes sir, there is. Dr. Sutton met with Mr. Jacobson yesterday and confronted him with the issue. He claims he can teach his class the way he wants, citing ‘academic freedom.’ Dr. Sutton’s meeting with Mr. Jacobson wasn’t very pleasant, and when he was totally uncooperative she recommended his removal from the classroom. Making a long story short, he appealed her decision to me, and we just met with Mr. Jacobson a few minutes ago. I think the best way for you to get a sense of what’s going on here is to let you listen to the recording of that meeting. It is about twenty minutes, but it will save a lot of time.”

Dr. Ford had brought his portable tape player, so Caraway said, “Okay, put the tape in and let’s hear it.”

After Caraway heard the tape, he commented, “Well, you were right, John. The tape tells the story pretty well. Mr. Jacobson seems to be on a tear about ‘academic freedom’ all of a sudden.” Caraway asked, “What does he mean by Dr. Sutton and Mr. Butler are out to get him?”

Dr. Sutton related the information about the previous complaints regarding the cheerleaders and athletes. She had brought Mr. Jacobson's personnel file with her, so she showed Dr. Caraway the letter Mr. Butler had placed in his file regarding that issue.

Caraway listened to parts of the tape again. The three of them discussed all the issues that had been covered with Jacobson since the first spring meeting. Caraway concluded that Ford and Sutton were right about the sensitivity of this issue. It clearly had implications of first amendment rights, and the "academic freedom" issue was a touchy subject these days.

John Ford spoke up, "Dr. Caraway, I'm the last one to say fire somebody, especially in the middle of the year, but this may be such a case. He's pretty belligerent about the fact he has 'rights' under 'academic freedom.' It sounds a little like he may have talked with a lawyer and may be trying to set us up for a lawsuit! I can't imagine why, but then the part about Mr. Butler and Dr. Sutton being 'out to get him' sounds like he's trying to set the stage for a lawsuit as well."

Caraway seemed somewhat on edge, "Lawsuit or no lawsuit, we need to do the best thing for the college. What are your thoughts about the possibility of a 'plan of improvement' for Mr. Jacobson? Do you think we can salvage him?"

Ford responded, "Dr. Caraway, I know how you feel about our providing opportunities for improvement, especially in lieu of dismissal; but in this case Mr. Jacobson has taken quite an antagonistic position and seems very determined to exercise what he thinks are his rights to 'academic freedom.' which of course are basic under the first amendment. I realize that if we terminate him we'll probably be risking legal action. I feel confident that he'll claim 'retaliation' because he has exercised freedom of speech."

Dr. Caraway asked, "Are you now saying we should try to work something out to avoid a lawsuit?"

"Not really. I guess what I'm saying is that I needed to write that letter. I really had no choice under the circumstances, given his belligerent behavior and his refusal to listen to reason. But you're the one who has to hear his appeal, and if you think he's salvageable, I'm okay with that."

"How about you, Dr. Sutton? Will you be okay with my working out some type of 'plan of improvement' – that is if he can take the 'high road' and promise me he won't cause any further problems?"

"Yes sir. If you're satisfied with his promise and feel that it'll work, I'm okay with it."

John Ford spoke up, "Dr. Caraway, it's just us talking, but can I be perfectly candid?"

"Of course, John."

"Well, sir, when we look back six months or so, we can easily see that this man's promise means nothing and that he can't be trusted. He promised Mr. Butler back in the spring that he wouldn't pick on cheerleaders and athletes after Butler called his hand on that. He reneged on that promise. Actually, that was a case of insubordination, and he could have been dismissed right then for that. As I look back on that, we probably should have.

In the current situation, he's become belligerent and is now accusing Dr. Sutton and Mr. Butler of plotting against him. I just think we may need to bite the bullet, take our chances and send him home."

"Melanie, do you agree with John's assessment?"

"In essence, yes. However, I really trust your judgment. I think you will know what to do after the appeal."

John Ford hastened to say, "Of course, we all trust your judgment, but you asked me for my thoughts, and I gave them to you."

"That you did, John. And I appreciate it very much, as always.

Okay. John, can you get me the letter of recommendation by sometime tomorrow?"

"Yes sir. I'll have it to you before mid-morning tomorrow."

"Good. I'll have Judy schedule an appointment for Mr. Jacobson just as soon as we can work it into the schedule. I'll let you know what I decide after the appeal. Is that all you had for now?"

Ford responded, "Yes sir."

Caraway dismissed Dr. Sutton with, "Thank you Dr. Sutton. Dr. Ford will bring you up to date after the appeal. I assume you have someone who can fill in for Mr. Jacobson in case this thing doesn't go well with him."

"Yes sir, we've got someone who can cover his classes just fine for the rest of the semester, and then we can look at finding a more permanent fix for the spring."

"Good. Thank you, Melanie. We'll keep you informed."

Sutton left the office.

Caraway turned to Ford, "John, be sure to keep Melanie in the loop on all of this."

"Yes sir, I will."

Caraway changed the subject, "I just need to give you a heads-up on a couple of matters."

Caraway gave Ford a brief review of what had happened regarding the possibility that John Casco would revive the issue of building an athletic complex on the home side of the football stadium. Caraway valued John Ford's opinion on matters like this, but he also wanted to let his number two man at the college know what was coming up.

"Dr. Caraway, I'm really surprised I haven't heard anything about this. I usually hear about things that are going on in the community, so maybe it's not too big of a deal yet. "

"Well, it might not be, but I think Mr. Casco's just keeping it close to the chest at this point. I just thought you needed to be aware that this could be an issue. We can always hope it just kind of goes away, but I don't think it will. By the way, you may want to check with Joe Biggers regarding the project I have him working on to get some facts in good order for the Board. You may have something to add, or maybe not, but you need to know what's happening, especially since it may involve some of the instructional programs – there may be some reference to the Health Occupations programs – Mr. Casco seems to be ready to point to those programs as the culprit that got the money that could have been spent for the athletic complex."

"I'll talk with Joe and offer my assistance in whatever way he needs me."

"Good. Well, John, I'm headed home for the day. You have a good night – I'll see you in the morning."

"You too, Dr. Caraway."

Caraway asked Judy to schedule an appointment for Jacobson the next day at three o'clock after his classes were over for the day. Before he left the office she had confirmed the appointment.

Caraway arrived home about six o'clock, and Margie was waiting with his glass of iced tea.

"Well, Charles, how was your day?"

"It was rather long, but productive. It makes the day go better when you feel like you are accomplishing something, and I think I made some progress today toward some type of resolution of some issues - at some point – if that makes any sense."

"Charles, it makes perfect sense. You were busy all day, you have a good number of irons in the fire, and nothing really got finished today, but you're hopeful for resolution at some point. Does that about do it?"

"Marge, you certainly have a way of expressing the complex in a simple fashion. What about your day?"

"Oh, I had a wonderful day. Mary, Glenda, Joyce (close friends from the community) and I had a 'ladies' day out' – we had lunch at the 'Old Southern Porch' (local antebellum home that was a bed and breakfast) & then we decided to go shopping in Jackson. I called and talked to

Judy, but you were in a meeting, and I didn't want to disturb you.

I found some really good bargains – I saved $176 on my purchases. Aren't you proud of me?"

"Well, how much did you spend to save that $176?"

"Oh, I really can't remember, but it was less than $300."

"That's really good Marge – that's better than thirty percent. I'm proud of you. What's for supper?"

"I got back in time to make your favorite salad with the mandarin oranges, the nuts, et cetera. I have some chicken strips in the oven to put in it. We can eat any time you're ready, but I thought we'd just enjoy the fall weather and the beauty of the foliage."

"Sounds good – I'm not in a hurry. We'll just finish off this pitcher of tea!"

CHAPTER NINE

Caraway was out early again on Wednesday morning. He made his usual visit to the maintenance facility and then went to the cafeteria for breakfast. He usually ate a light breakfast at home, but he felt like mixing with students this morning. He prized himself in knowing many of the students and enjoyed visiting with them out on campus. He had learned from a president he'd worked for in Texas the importance of being seen and accessible to students as well as faculty and staff. But, besides that, he enjoyed getting to know today's students. They can teach you a lot about your institution if you will simply listen and be open to what they're saying.

Caraway actually got to his office before Judy, which was almost unheard of, because she was always early! Judy was a country girl; she'd been raised on a farm and was an early riser. She drove over twenty-five miles to work every day, and still got there before most people on campus. She also had the best work ethic of anyone he knew, and to top it off, she was super organized. She kept Caraway on track!

Caraway used the quiet time early in the morning when he did get to the office earlier than others to think about major issues. This morning those issues included what he would do about George Jacobson. This guy had been at the college some thirty years as a full time instructor in political science. Caraway had only known him for the past two years, but he remembered the evaluations for those years, and they had been above average. He was a widower with three children and several grandchildren. Why would he after all this time go off the deep end with the "academic freedom" issue and risk his reputation? Charles couldn't get a handle on this – it just defied his imagination. Maybe national politics had just put him over the edge.

Something else that crept into his head this morning was the issue that Barry Smith was working on. Again, Charles just couldn't get a handle on why Thomas Mitchell would be involved in getting pornographic material on his computer. He too, even more so, was risking his reputation, career and livelihood by what he was doing. Unlike George, however, Tom had a family at home, and he didn't have enough years to retire. Why? Why? Why?

Judy quietly knocked on the door at 7:45 to let Caraway know she was in the office. He greeted her good morning and asked her to update him on his appointments for the morning. She indicated there were a couple that he didn't have on his schedule yet. He quickly realized that his appointments would take him through lunch.

"Judy, I should get a letter from Dr. Ford this morning. It's important that I see it ASAP, but between appointments."

"Yes sir."

"Would you see if you can get Mr. Burchfield on the phone for me after my nine o'clock appointment?"

"Yes sir."

Caraway was thankful that his morning appointments on this day at least didn't bring serious issues or problems to solve. Most of them were actually rather pleasant meetings.

Judy buzzed Caraway at nine-thirty to tell him that Mr. Burchfield was on the line. Caraway brought Burchfield up to date on the Jacobson matter. He really had little hope of being able to salvage Mr. Jacobson. Burchfield told him that if he thought he would at some point have to take a stand on this instructor, better now than later after more damage was done.

Caraway felt a little better that the Board attorney had agreed with his assessment, but he still didn't look forward to the meeting with Jacobson. His last meeting of the morning was with Rebecca Newman, advisor for the campus Phi Theta Kappa (PTK) chapter. She had asked for a few minutes to discuss a new project for the chapter.

PTK is an international scholastic organization for two year college students. It was formed in 1918 as an honorary scholastic society to recognize scholarship among two-year college students. The organization provides many opportunities for students to excel in scholarship, as well as leadership, on the home campus and beyond at state, regional and international levels. The PTK chapter at Fair Oaks had become an outstanding organization for the college and had been recognized several times at the international level as one of the top twenty-five chapters in the organization of over twelve hundred chapters worldwide. Caraway had previous experience with the PTK organization in Texas as Dean, and he knew going in as President of Fair Oaks the great benefit of this student organization.

Rebecca told Caraway about the chapter's new project to provide a tutorial program for elementary students in the local school. Caraway was asked to approve the project in light of policy that required him to approve any new program by a student group that involved local schools. He did so enthusiastically, and he commended Rebecca on the outstanding job she was doing as advisor of the chapter.

fter lunch, Judy asked if Dr. Ford could have about thirty minutes in the afternoon sometime around two o'clock.

"Of course, tell him one-thirty would be better. I'd like a little time for reflection before I meet with Mr. Jacobson at three."

When Dr. Ford came at one-thirty, he said, "We have a situation that you probably need to be aware of regarding the search for an Assistant Dean for Career Tech. I appointed a screening committee to accept applications and screen applicants for that position. Of course, I involved Dr. Dupree, and as customary, she receives the recommendation from the committee, then me and then you for final approval to go to the Board. All of this is according to our normal procedure."

"I'm with you; go ahead."

"Well, the committee received fourteen applications. There were six that didn't meet the requirements for some reason or other; the committee screened another five applicants on the basis of paperwork and reference checks. So, they interviewed three people last week. Dr. Dupree received the recommendation from the committee on Friday – they were very high on a Mr. Carl Woods who had pretty extensive experience in a like position at Cascade High School (a high school within the college district). As a matter of fact they were locked in to Mr. Woods to get the job."

"I think I see where this is going. Go ahead."

"Dr. Dupree has looked over the three applicants very closely. She does not agree at all with the committee's decision, and she wants to recommend a different person entirely. She knows how valuable the screening committee process is to the system, and she believes in it wholeheartedly; she also believes in getting the 'right person for the job' – not only that, she's aware of your emphasis on that as well. She felt strongly enough about this that she met with the committee chairman and asked for his take on the applicants. He indicated that the committee was very strong for Mr. Woods. The committee was split four to one for Mr. Woods at first, but Mary Dunlop, the fifth person, came around after a while. I really think she may have been a little intimidated by the other four members.

Dr. Dupree came to see me yesterday and asked my advice on how to handle this situation. I think she may have lost confidence in the committee. She was so upset about this that I asked her to give me a brief run through on the three applicants. Of course, I haven't interviewed them, so I'm depending on her perceptions mostly, but I think she may be justified in her concerns at this point. I asked her to give me a little while to think this through – I told her I might discuss it with you as well.

She seems to have a real dilemma here - on the one hand, she doesn't want to upstage or overrule the committee, especially when they're so adamant about the applicant they want to hire, but she wants the best person for the job – she *feels* that's someone other than Mr. Woods."

"John, this is not Dr. Dupree's first rodeo. Why didn't she just sit down and talk with the committee and explain her position and have them take another look at the applicants. Or she might have said 'this is my position and here's why - I think another applicant is the right person.' So, John, tell me straight – what's going on here?"

"Dr. Caraway, I think there are two things ....off the record somewhat at this point?"

"Okay, go ahead."

"One, Jimmy Bell is the most adamant committee member, according to Dr. Dupree. She was reluctant to tell me this, because she got it in confidence from the committee chairman, but Bell made statements during committee deliberations that went something like, 'Why are we even meeting anyway? The administration will pick who they want, so we're wasting our time on this silly process.'"

Caraway responded, "That's not the first time someone has accused us of manipulating things to hire who we want, so what's different this time?"

"The second thing may be a cause for more concern."

"Okay, I'm listening."

"Well, as you know I've been around a while, and I know the connections better than most as far as politics go. Bennett West (member of Board of Supervisors in Concord County) is a good friend of Sidney Woods, Carl Woods' dad. My suspicion is that there's been a contact by Mr. Sidney Woods about his son's application."

"John, it is also not that unusual that a county supervisor would contact us about an applicant……hmm, but most of the time the contact is with one of us and we know how to deal with that, but a committee member might be influenced in some way….. I guess I see your point."

Caraway continued, "Do you have anything besides your hunch to indicate there's been such a contact?"

"Not at this point, but I can do some checking, with your approval. I don't want to stir up a hornet's nest here; and I don't think I will if I can be discrete enough, but I want you to give the okay before I take a chance."

"John, what do you want to do?"

"I think first of all that we need to delay the selection process for a week and have Dr. Dupree tell the committee that in light of the importance of this particular position you and I are going to do a full interview with the applicants – at least I need to interview them. An extended process is not that unusual – we've done it several times through the years."

Ford continued, "You set the bar on how important it is to hire the best person for a job without undue influence. Our policy is well written, and we follow it.....we don't need to let this situation get us off track. I think if we don't listen to Dr. Dupree we're going to regret it. We could be setting a precedent for hiring someone who knows the right politician but who's not the best applicant.

I also need to personally check the references on these three as well.

I realize the ball is in my court at this point, but I also know that it will be in your court shortly; I want to be sure we're on the same page before I take action that might put you in a difficult position."

Caraway responded, "Okay, can you give this a top priority today?"

"Absolutely. It may take me a couple of days to reach all the people on reference checks, but I can at least start to get a feel for things today.

I thought I'd get Mavis (John Ford's secretary) to go ahead and set up interviews for the three finalists – I can devote

Thursday of next week to that. I hope to be able to give you a final report by that Friday afternoon. Will you have time to interview the top three applicants next Thursday?"

"I'll make time – I'll rearrange my schedule if I need to - get with Judy to set up the times."

"Thank you – I'll get right on it."

"John, let me know if you get into that hornet's nest, will you?"

"Yes sir."

Caraway's meeting with Ford was over at about two fifteen. He used the time before Jacobson's appeal to prepare himself mentally for the meeting. He still couldn't understand what had gotten into Jacobson to just go off the deep end like that after thirty years with an unblemished record. His mind was made up about what he was going to do, but he needed some quiet time to think through how he would do it.

Caraway was still sorting everything out in his mind when three o'clock came. Judy buzzed and announced, "Dr. Caraway, Mr. Jacobson is here for his appointment. Would you like me to send him in?"

"No, Judy. I'll be right there." Caraway thought he'd get the meeting off to a good start by personally inviting Jacobson into the office.

"Mr. Jacobson, please come in."

"Thank you, Dr. Caraway."

Breaking somewhat from protocol, Caraway had decided to meet at his round table. He knew this was an appeal and an "official" meeting, but somehow he felt he'd have a better chance of accomplishing his goal if he could just ratchet down the tension a bit. He invited Jacobson to sit at the table.

Jacobson had been in the President's office several times during his thirty years at Fair Oaks, but only once while Dr. Caraway had held the office; on that occasion he had sat in front of the desk. Today was different, and it caught him off guard just a bit.

Once they were seated Caraway said as he turned on the portable tape recorder, "Mr. Jacobson, since this visit is for an appeal of Dr. Ford's recommendation for termination, I need to have an official record. If you wish to have a copy of the tape afterwards, just let me know." Caraway had heard the tape of his meeting with Ford and Sutton, so he preempted the question that was coming about a copy of the tape.

"Thank you, Dr. Caraway. I would like a copy."

"Sure, I'll have one made and make it available before the end of the week." Caraway was thinking, *if he has talked with an attorney about this, he'll ask for a copy sooner, because he'll want to get it to the attorney when he meets with him/her, and that will be very soon.*

"Dr. Caraway, I'd like to go ahead and get a copy in the morning if that's okay."

"I'm sure we can arrange that. Just come by after nine o'clock and ask Judy for it.

"Thank you."

"Now, George, I want to hear your side of all of this. What's going on about the politics in class?"

"Dr. Caraway, I've been teaching here for thirty years, and I've never had a problem making my own decisions about the class syllabus and how I teach it.

Caraway caught the word "syllabus" and had a thought. "George, you don't happen to have a copy of that syllabus with you, do you?" He knew full well he didn't.

"Well, no. Do I need one?"

"Oh no. I just wondered how much of the 'political' stuff you had in there. Just off the top of your head, do you remember how much, what percentage, of the lessons are on the subject of 'politics'?"

Jacobson thought he saw where this was going, and he was prepared. He said, "Dr. Caraway, that syllabus hasn't been revised in several years. I doubt seriously that there's much beyond the very basic principles of government in there. A syllabus has to be revised once in a while to reflect the times. Since I'm the only full-time faculty member who teaches government, I just haven't bothered to bring it up to date."

"George, we may be a bit off track with this discussion, but I'm just curious. If you had revised the syllabus, say last year, what percentage of class time would have been about 'politics' versus principles of government?"

Jacobson thought for a moment before answering. "Dr. Caraway, I see where you're going with this. I know the syllabus has to be approved by the Division Chair, and I know that Mr. Butler or Dean Sutton would probably not have approved one with a significant percentage of material about the 'political realm' of government. Nevertheless, I think it's important, and I think I have the right to teach it."

Caraway had set the trap, and Jacobson had seen it, but too late. He had stepped right in it. "I see. Well, George, you do remember that the Faculty Handbook has a section about teaching to the syllabus, don't you? Since you're a government instructor and you deal with laws and rulings all the time, you know the importance of having a standard of sorts that everyone follows – to an extent that is."

"Dr. Caraway, you are a fairly conservative guy, and I'm sure you're aware of the fact that the 'liberals' have taken over in Washington. Don't you see why it's so important that we inform people of what's happening?"

"George, I consider myself to be more conservative than liberal; however, I have a responsibility to run a college without letting my personal political views enter into my decision-making. Likewise, you should not let your personal views enter into your teaching in the classroom."

"I understand what you're saying, but I just feel so strongly about this. Somebody's got to do something about big government invading our personal freedoms!"

"George, how many years do you have in the retirement system? Of course, you have thirty here at Fair Oaks and probably some leave time built up. Have you looked at what your earnings would be if you retired – have you thought about that?"

"As a matter of fact, yes, I have, and I would make almost as much after taxes, as I make now. I will have a total of thirty-four years in the retirement system, plus some leave time built up, and I'll be eligible for Social Security benefits in a couple of years. That would really put me over the top. But I enjoy teaching government."

"George, I detect that some of your enthusiasm for 'government' may have given way to your political agenda. Am I off track here?"

Jacobson considered what he would say next, because he had definitely lost some of his zeal for government over the past several years. Actually, he didn't enjoy it much anymore, but that's not usually something you tell your boss. Finally, Jacobson managed to say, "I guess my teaching has lost some of the excitement of the earlier years, but I make up for that with the level of expertise I have from thirty years of teaching. On the other hand, yes, I have considered retirement over the past year or so."

Caraway just looked at him, and said, "Well? Maybe your retirement would allow you to devote some time to the things you enjoy but haven't had time for in the past."

Jacobson responded, "Let me ask you this. Would the college let me out of my contract at the end of this semester?"

"George, the contract can be voided on mutual agreement between you and the college. I'll be glad to recommend to the Board that you be allowed to retire in December if that's what you want. I'm pretty sure they will approve it on my recommendation."

"Let's say I retired in December, would I be allowed to teach part-time?"

"George, that depends. If you give me a commitment that you'll get back to the basics of teaching government, then I'll recommend that Dr. Sutton use you for part-time work. I would expect you to honor that commitment, and if you didn't, we'd be right back here, with a different ending."

"Can I have 'til in the morning to think about this?"

Caraway responded, "George, you have thirty years of a fine reputation here at Fair Oaks. You need to make the right decision here. Of course, I'll give you 'til tomorrow morning, but I do need to have a decision, so that I can stay on track with the appeals process."

"Are you going to confirm my termination, if I decide I want to stay?"

Caraway reflected on that question for just a moment before he said, "George, you'll find that out only if you decide not to retire."

"Okay. I have a nine o'clock class. Can I see you before then?"

"That works fine for me. I'm free from eight fifteen 'til nine."

"Good, I'll see you at eight-fifteen."

"Have a good evening, George."

They shook hands in a professional manner as Jacobson left the office.

Caraway's Thursday morning in the office was busy with checking email and other routine matters until eight-fifteen when Judy buzzed to tell him George Jacobson was there to see him.

Caraway asked her to tell him to come in.

Caraway greeted him at the door, "Good morning, George. Come in."

"Good morning, Dr. Caraway. This won't take long. I've been thinking about our discussion yesterday, and I've made probably one of the biggest decisions of my life."

"George, I'm glad you've given this some serious thought."

"Dr. Caraway, I'm handing in my letter of resignation, effective at the end of this semester. I hate to leave the Dean and Mr. Butler with a vacancy in the middle of the year, but I think this is best. I've done a lot of soul-searching over the past twelve hours, and I just think it's time for me to step down. Yesterday you said I had a good reputation here; I got to thinking about that. I appreciate your recognizing that, and I think I do too. I've had some good years here, made a lot of friends, but it's time to go. I don't agree with Dr. Sutton's analysis of my class time, and I'd have to fight for my right to teach as I think best if I stayed. As strongly as I feel about the policies in Washington and my right to talk about that in my class, I just don't think I'd feel right about the battle we'd have over all that."

Caraway had to ask, "What about the next two months of classes? Are you okay with the guidelines you'll have to follow regarding the class time?"

"Oh yes, I've thought about that - I can handle it. I still don't think it's right, but I'll keep my philosophy and complaints about Washington to myself. As a matter of fact, I plan to pay Dr. Sutton a visit later today – I need to apologize to her. I'm her senior in age, but she's still by boss, and I wasn't too respectful to her when we met. I need to feel better about all of that – don't want any hard feelings."

"George, I think Dr. Sutton will be very gracious when you meet with her. I think I understand perfectly what you're saying about your decision to retire. I think you're making a good decision. If I may ask, what will you do in retirement?"

"I'm going to visit with family – haven't had much chance to do that for a long time. I'll see how that goes and then see what comes next."

Caraway's sincerity was apparent when he said, "George, let me know if I can help you in the retirement process."

They shook hands. As Jacobson began to move toward the door, he turned and said, "About that tape from yesterday, I won't be needing that after all."

Caraway thought for a moment he was going to get emotional, but it passed. He responded, "That's fine, George. If you change your mind, it'll be on file in my office."

After his meeting with Jacobson, he went down to John Ford's office and gave him the good news. They both felt relieved. They still had to get through the next two and half months with Jacobson in the classroom, but somehow they felt that he would protect his reputation as promised.

Caraway left the office at eleven-thirty to go give his speech to the Rotary Club in a nearby town. Caraway enjoyed speaking to civic groups about the college. It always provided a good opportunity to talk about the college programs and the fact that the college really was a part of the community. In his speech to Rotary he'd talked primarily about instructional programs, athletics and the administrative structure of the community college system within the state.

Caraway had learned many years ago that when speaking to a civic club at lunch, you always made it a point to end the talk after about twenty minutes, or no later than 12:55 PM, whichever came first. He knew the people in attendance were business leaders in the community who had allocated time for the lunch meeting, but who needed to be on the way back to work by one o'clock. Today he had ended his talk at about ten minutes before one o'clock and asked if there were questions.

The first question was about athletics, and Caraway was able to provide a quick answer, leaving time for a second question. The second question was, "Dr. Caraway, you mentioned that the State Board for Community Colleges in Mississippi is a 'coordinating' board that has limited authority over the local colleges. Can you tell us why you think Mississippi has the best model, as opposed to a chancellor model like you would find in other states?"

"Thank you for that question. I'll be happy to discuss this issue. First, the local autonomy of the colleges in Mississippi was set out in statute back in the 1920s when the first 'junior' colleges were formed. The 'Local Board' concept provides local control by the leadership within each college's community. That model has actually served the state of Mississippi well through the years. The fact that community leaders are involved in the governance of the colleges throughout the state provides a local political base that has significant influence in the state legislature. This model also allows the local community a great voice in the direction of their college.

Now, the best thing about the Mississippi system is that we have a very strong State Board that also has legislative clout, but it just doesn't have the day-to-day control over the administration of each of the colleges. By the way, the Executive Director of the State Board does a great job of speaking throughout the state on behalf of the system. In addition, he is greatly respected by members of the state legislature and does an outstanding job of representing the interest of all the colleges there.

On the issue of state control, I might just add that there are policies and procedures that are adopted by the State Board that provide guidance for all fifteen colleges. The State Board is responsible for divvying up the money that's provided by the state legislature according to a formula that is agreed upon by everyone. So in essence, we have the best of both worlds in Mississippi – strength in both local and state venues. We have a very strong community college 'system,' one that has been cited by two different national groups as being in the top five in the country."

Caraway had used up his ten minutes left for questions, but he talked with several people individually after the meeting before heading back to his office.

The rest of the day was rather routine for Caraway, with various meetings across campus. He enjoyed the opportunity to get out of the office for a while on Thursday afternoon and mix with members of the faculty and staff. He always learned something from being out on campus.

Friday proved to be a different story.

CHAPTER TEN

On Friday morning Caraway was a little surprised when Barry Smith called and asked for a time to meet. He really thought he wouldn't hear from him until early the next week, but he was glad to get this news because he was ready to close the book on the computer security issue. He asked Judy to schedule a time late in the day so he and Barry would have an opportunity to talk without interruption. Whatever the results of Barry's investigation, he knew the conversation would probably not be short, and he knew for sure it needed to be very confidential.

Caraway spent some time before the meeting with Barry Smith in deep thought as to what action he was going to have to take about Thomas Mitchell. He had insisted that Barry rule out any possibility that someone else had hacked into Mitchell's computer or that someone had simply gone into his office when he wasn't there and used it to download this stuff onto a flash drive. Anyway, that possibility seemed even more remote now than last week when they talked about it. Caraway even felt a little reserved about his decision, but he knew he did the right thing – he could not in good conscience approach Mitchell when he wasn't sure about his guilt, not if there was any other way.

Barry showed up at 4:30 just as Judy was leaving for the day.

"Well, Barry, you've either found a short cut to your work, or you've spent some serious time over the past few days ferreting out this information. I'm anxious to get this settled, so give me the bottom line."

"Dr. Caraway, I don't know how to begin. This has turned out to be my worst nightmare."

"What do you mean *your* worst nightmare? Has something *else* happened?"

"Oh, no sir, not with Mr. Mitchell. It's just that the old saying, 'nothing is as it seems' has a special meaning in this case."

"Are you telling me that the one percent factor we discussed turned out to have merit – someone else *did* use Mitchell's computer?"

"Actually, yes sir, I am, but I'm afraid I have some really bad news – actually, it's more bad news for me than anyone else."

"Ok, let's hear it!"

"Phil Turner (one of Barry's technicians) is the guilty party."

"What?"

"Let me start at the beginning."

"Please do!"

"I worked on this over the weekend, and I had planned to work late on Monday night to try and get a lot done – I really had hoped I could knock it out by mid-week. Well, Phil just kept hanging around on Monday, and it seemed kind of funny because he really didn't need to be there. I even told him to go home; it had been a long day. He just said he needed to finish up some things. To be honest, he acted a little suspicious. I decided at about 6:30 that he was going to be there awhile, so I said good night and left. I went down to the coffee shop and had a cup of coffee and drove back by at about 7:30 – he was still there. I just went on home.

The next day I asked Phil how late he worked and why he needed to put in time after hours. He just shrugged and said he'd worked an hour or so after I left and he had some things he needed to finish up – he does have a pretty heavy work load right now, but nothing he can't handle during normal work hours.

I didn't like the way this all felt. I really didn't suspect he was involved in the Mitchell situation, but I did become more suspicious that he was doing something that he didn't want me to know about. Something was wrong with this picture.

So, you remember that we've installed cameras around campus and have gotten pretty good at disguising them as something else. I decided I wanted to know about Phil, so I went to work early on Tuesday and put a camera in one of our smoke detector cases that faces Phil's work station.

I made a point of leaving a little early on Tuesday so he could do whatever he wanted after hours. I actually had the camera set up so I could watch real time, so I went over to the computer lab to remote in and watch. Phil didn't waste much time – he began downloading the porno stuff within a half hour after I left. On checking later I found that he had done it through Mr. Mitchell's computer. I can't tell you how shocked I was at this. I mean, I never would have thought Phil would do something like this. He is one of my best technicians!"

"Does Phil know you know?"

"I'm pretty sure he doesn't – I'm still in a bit of a shock, but I think everything's fairly normal."

"So, you found this out on Tuesday night. This is Friday. I assume you've done some further investigating to determine exactly how he did this and to what extent?"

"Yes sir."

"Are there other computers that he's used besides Mitchell's, and by the way, does this absolutely rule out that one percent we discussed – Mitchell is off the hook? "

"I think it's safe to say Mr. Mitchell is off the hook, and yes, there are other computers, but not personal ones.

Wednesday night was my time at the shop – Phil had done his thing on Tuesday, and I figured he might go on home on Wednesday, so I was prepared to work late. Once I knew that Phil was doing this, I had given it some thought later Tuesday night, and to be honest, I was somewhat preoccupied with it during the day on Wednesday. It's really not so hard when you have the skills like Phil and have the right equipment. I have to tell you – I began to feel a little dirty. You see, you and everyone else at this college trust me and my department with a tremendous responsibility, and that trust goes so deep – we have access to virtually everything at the college. I felt like we'd betrayed that trust."

"Barry, you had no way of knowing this until now. You don't need to beat yourself up over this – you took immediate action when you thought Tom Mitchell was the guilty party, and now you've ferreted out the real guilty party. That trust has not been betrayed by you or your department; only one person has violated that trust, and that's Phil."

"I still feel like there's something I could have done, and I almost got an innocent person in serious trouble."

"Barry, you've more than made up for Phil's sins, and now you've exonerated Mr. Mitchell."

"Thanks to you, sir! Anyway, I actually got into Phil's computer in the shop and saw exactly how he had gotten into other computers. There are actually three others – and guess what - they are all in the computer lab."

"No other personal computers were involved? That's strange. Why pick on Tom Mitchell?"

"Well, the only thing I can come up with is that he was thinking that if, just if, someone stumbled onto what was going on, he might need a fall guy. Really, I guess it almost worked."

"You mean he suspected that you might see the stuff coming through the filter and start looking; and if the only computers used were in the lab and they were used during a time the lab was closed, you would look closer. And if you didn't find a 'fall guy' you'd start looking even closer, and you'd stand a much better chance of finding the truth."

"That's about it. Anyway, it really doesn't matter. I spent some time on his computer Wednesday night, and I'm satisfied that I'm at the bottom of it. We're clean now, that is unless Phil does this again. So, how do you intend to handle this? I hate to lose a good technician, but I'm ready for him to be out of my department! I can't trust him!"

Caraway interrupted, "We haven't covered the email situation. Remember, he was exchanging emails with someone named Wendy; I assume from your earlier comment that she was using computers in the computer lab. What was going on there?"

"Oh, yeah, I almost forgot. I solved that too by placing a camera in the computer lab to see who was getting on after hours. I knew it had to be someone with a key, because it was always after hours. Anyway, Darlene Doss is the one who's been trading emails with Phil. She's one of the part-time lab monitors who work off hours, so she has to have a key to get in and lock up."

"Was there anything in the emails to indicate that Phil knows who 'Wendy' is?"

"I didn't see anything, and I really don't think he does."

Barry responded, "Judging from the emails, what do you think was going on, really?"

"Dr. Caraway, I think it's a simple matter of having fun with cybersex. The novelty of it sometimes is attractive in and of itself. It's pretty kinky stuff, if you know what I mean."

"Ok, Barry. You've done an outstanding job on all of this, from the time you first mentioned it to me to now. We need to bring Dr. Ford up to date on this situation. After all you do report to him, you know."

"Yes sir. "

"It's Friday and it's rather late, is there a chance Phil is in your shop now?"

"No sir, I don't think so. He's already gone for the weekend. I think he was going out of town this weekend."

"Barry, why don't you keep the camera on and record what happens over the weekend, just to be sure we'll know if we have some more repair work. As a matter of fact, if you see him in there over the weekend, call me on my cell."

"Yes sir."

"When Phil arrives for work on Monday morning, you tell him that Dr. Ford and I want to see the two of you and bring him up to my office. I'll brief Dr. Ford over the weekend to be sure he's up to speed on all of this.

We'll get Phil's keys, of course. You need to make a list of whatever else he might have that we need to collect. And Barry, I know you're aware that you need to change all the passwords and take extra precautions against future problems."

Barry answered, "That's in the works – I'm all set to do that after our meeting with Phil.

Dr. Caraway, when can I look for a replacement? I'm really going to be in a bind on work load when I don't have Phil. "

"You can get an announcement out after our meeting on Monday."

"Yes sir. One more thing – will this become public or will it be like a resignation by Phil?"

"As far as I'm concerned, in the interest of protecting the college from bad PR, it can be handled quietly, but that will depend on Phil. Now, let's go home."

"Have a good weekend, sir."

"You too, Barry."

CHAPTER ELEVEN

Caraway was glad to see the weekend come, although it had not been such a bad week in terms of end results. He had closed the file on the Susie Jones case, and the mystery of who was getting through the firewall with pornography had been solved; actually, Barry Smith had solved this, but Caraway was definitely the beneficiary of Barry's good work – the case wasn't closed, but he knew where he was going with it on Monday. Caraway was also thankful that the matter of George Jacobson had had a good ending with his voluntary retirement.

There was still the matter of the Assistant Career Tech Dean's position that wasn't yet settled, but he and John Ford would interview the top three candidates for that position next week and hopefully bring that to an acceptable closure. He tried to shove all this aside, but he knew he would have recurring thoughts before the weekend was over. Right now, Caraway just wanted to get out of the office and relax on the deck with Margie and a tall glass of iced tea.

When he arrived home Margie was waiting on the deck. The weather absolutely defined the fall season to the superlative. The leaves on the Ginkgo trees in the back yard were a showcase of beautiful yellow, with just a hint of orange; and the weather was getting cool and crisp.

"Charles, I was just about to call you. You usually get home earlier on Friday afternoon – why are you running late?"

"I just had a few things I needed to finish up before the weekend. I'll start with a bang on Monday morning, and I didn't want to have things hanging unfinished."

Charles and Margie sat on the deck and talked until dark, just chatting. Both were interested in keeping up with state and national politics to some extent, so they discussed the up-coming election in November and their favorite candidates. They were true southern conservatives in their basic beliefs, and thought that the federal government was getting too involved in the day to day lives of people these days. Charles couldn't help but think about George Jacobson and the fact that he'd pushed his beliefs onto students during class time.

Saturday night's football game was at home, and Margie had suggested in light of the wonderful weather that they invite the visiting president and his wife to come early for an afternoon cookout, in lieu of the traditional meal in the private dining room. Charles thought that was a great idea, but he had already told President Homer Turnage that the meal would be at 5:30 in the private dining room. Margie told him that she'd taken care of that – she had discussed it with the food service department and had talked with Homer's wife Annette. Everything was set.

Charles was pleased that Margie had taken charge of the meal for their guests. He depended a great deal on the First Lady to know how to entertain guests at the President's home. Besides, Homer and Annette had become best friends with Charles and Margie, and they were special; and the weather was just too good to waste with an inside meal.

Margie had invited John Ford and his wife, Vicki, to join them as well. John had known Dr. Turnage for many years and was a good friend. John had also become a very good friend of Charles, as well as his very competent VP for Instruction at the college.

Homer and Annette Turnage had arrived early as Margie and Annette had planned, so there would be time for a good visit. Homer had been President of Britton

Community College for over twenty-five years and was considered to be one of the icons in the Presidents' Association. Prior to his presidency, he had been a high school principal and a county superintendant. He was well past the age of seventy, and he was still going strong.

The ladies visited while the men talked about what was happening in the world of education, particularly the up-coming legislative session where funding of community colleges was a major issue. Homer had served as the Legislative Chairman of the Presidents' Association for many years and had made a strong case to the Legislative Budget Committee a few weeks ago during the normal hearing process. However, the real work was still ahead. The three men talked about strategy for the up-coming session of the state legislature.

The excitement level at the football game was "over the top," with a very close game throughout, but the Bulldogs had finally won in double overtime. Since it was a very important conference game, the students wanted a trophy of this win, so they headed for the goal post with the intent of taking it down. Thankfully the Campus Police had warning that something like this might happen, and they'd been around long enough to know how students react, so they were ready with reinforcements from the local sheriff's department, as well as the local PD.

Caraway was proud of his officers and the fact that reinforcements were available when needed. The situation had been contained without major incident. Some of the students had been removed from the scene and taken to Dr. Summerset's office for discipline after they had not heeded the warning to leave the goal post intact, but no serious problems had developed as a result of the incident.

Charles and Margie especially enjoyed this Sunday as a day of worship, but also a day of rest. Sunday afternoon provided a special time of relaxation. Both enjoyed a good book. Margie had finished Grisham's latest book and was starting on a new book by David Baldacci. Charles had been so busy over the past few weeks that he had abandoned a good Vince Flynn novel a couple of weeks ago and had to stretch his memory somewhat to pick up the story line. The phone didn't ring once that afternoon!

Monday morning came too soon for Charles. He didn't get out on campus quite as early as usual because he knew it would be a long, and possibly trying day. When he arrived in the office at eight o'clock, Judy already had a couple of phone messages for him. One was from Barry Smith saying that everything was fine – no change over the weekend. Caraway noted there was an appointment for Barry and Phil to see him and Dr. Ford later in the morning. The other was a message to call Batson County Supervisor Robert Case. Batson County was one of his supporting counties, so he decided he'd take care of that call early. Case probably wanted to recommend someone for something.

Caraway had Judy get Mr. Case on the line.

"Good morning, Mr. Case. How are things in Batson County this morning?"

"Well, Dr. Caraway, they're not so good, but I hope you can help me change that."

"What's the problem?"

"I'm sure you were at the ballgame Saturday night – that was one of the best games I've ever seen. Congratulations on a big win for the Bulldogs."

"Thank you. But what things do we need to change this morning to make things better?"

"Dr. Caraway, I'm sure you are aware of the incident where students wanted to get the goal post down to celebrate the win."

"Yes sir. I was very proud of how our Campus PD handled that situation; and I appreciate the Batson County Sheriff's Department having deputies there to help."

"Well, Mr. Bob Devlin (local businessman who had a son at Fair Oaks) called me Sunday and told me his son had been tased at the game; he said he had a big red place where the taser had been used. He was one of those arrested and taken to jail that night."

"Mr. Case, I haven't heard about any tazing at the game, and I think I would have if it had happened, but I'll sure check on this. But I need to correct one thing now. The boys were not taken to jail – they were taken to Student Services and had to talk with Dr. Summerset that night. I'm sure there will be some form of discipline to follow."

"Are you sure they weren't taken to jail, because Mr. Devlin seemed pretty sure."

"Mr. Case, it's hard to be sure of anything these days, but I would know if they had been taken to jail. Just to satisfy the question, however, I'll definitely check on that too."

"Thank you Dr. Caraway. I appreciate your cooperation on this."

"By the way, Mr. Case, do you know why Mr. Devlin called you instead of someone at the college?"

"Dr. Caraway, you know how things work in politics. People elect you to office as a public servant, and they think you're supposed to be at their disposal to handle most any kind of problem that comes along. The thing is, they may not have even voted for you in the first place!"

"Mr. Case, I appreciate your call. I'll do my best to get back to you with an answer to your questions before the day's out."

"Thank you, Dr. Caraway. By the way, we've finalized our budget for next year, and we've given the college a 3% increase over last year. I know that's not much in light of your problems with reduced state funding, but maybe it'll help some."

"Thank you, Mr. Case. Every little bit helps. We appreciate your support."

"Good. You have a good day, and let me know if I can ever help you or the college."

"You have a good day too Mr. Case!"

When Caraway hung up the phone he immediately called Robert Summerset and asked him the two questions he had just been asked. Summerset assured him no one went to jail. Caraway had a thought – had handcuffs been used? Summerset once again assured him that no, they had not.

When he asked about the use of a taser by one of the officers, Summerset's answers became a little less certain.

"Dr. Caraway, two of our officers, Chief Howard and Officer Ralph Sessions, are certified to use a taser, but I'm pretty sure they didn't. They would've told me about that.

I'm not sure if the town PD or the Sheriff's Department deputies even had tasers, but I'll talk to the Chief."

"Robert, I need to know the answer to this question ASAP. I'm like you, I think we would've known about this had it happened, but I need to positively rule it out. And if, by some chance, a taser was used by one of our officers, I want to see the officer in my office five minutes ago!"

"Yes sir."

"Now, if another officer used a taser, I want to know who and from what department just as quick!"

"Yes sir."

Caraway was pretty sure as he thought about the situation that he would have known about the use of a taser on campus, but he could not let this get out of hand. Rumors could often cause more harm than the facts, even when the facts were bad.

On the other hand, Caraway was thinking......*what if a taser was used? Officers are trained to use those things to avoid more drastic measures. No officer is certified to carry a taser until he's properly trained, which includes having a taser used on himself. Anyway, I won't feel good about this until I know for sure a taser wasn't used on a college kid – on my campus.*

Caraway was jarred back to real time when he got a buzz from Judy indicating that Phil Turner and Barry Smith were there early to see him and Dr. Ford.

Caraway asked her to let Dr. Ford know – ask the other gentlemen to wait, but send Dr. Ford in when he got there. He took a minute to clear his head from the previous phone call. Monday was definitely off to a bang!

As he thought about Phil Turner, he was sure he was going to terminate him, but he wasn't sure about whether to bring charges. He knew he was guilty of some type of wire fraud, probably a federal offense, but the other things were not so much illegal as they were just plain unethical and unprofessional to the superlative. Anyway, he'd see what kind of attitude Phil had about it all before he decided anything beyond the termination. Today's meeting was primarily to take care of campus business. He could discuss any charges with the college attorney and local law enforcement officials later – if that became necessary. He'd leave the options open for now.

John Ford came in with a little smile on his face.

"What're you smiling about, John?"

"Dr. Caraway, I'm sorry, I just can't help it. I know it's not right, but that young man out there had a look on his face like he was about to jump in a lake full of alligators – come to think of it, it only takes one gator to bite a plug out of your rear end, and something tells me he's about to meet with one. I'm sorry, I know that was unprofessional, but it was just too good to pass up."

"John, do you think we need to press charges against Phil?"

"Well, I'd like to get an attitude check on him when you talk with him before I answer that one. Besides, you have plenty of time to do that anyway."

"My thoughts, exactly. Let's get him in here and get this done. I've got other things to do today."

Caraway buzzed Judy, "Judy, send in Barry Smith & Phil Turner."

"Good morning gentlemen. Phil, I'll get right down to the reason we're here. We have uncovered information about Mr. Thomas Mitchell's computer being used to bring pornography through the filter. What can you tell me about that?"

"Wait! You mean Mr. Mitchell has been getting through the security filter on our system to download porn on his computer?"

Caraway gave Phil a hard look for a sustained moment - the room fell silent.

Finally, he said, Phil, "Why do you think you are here today?" There was another long pause – his look said it all. Phil just looked at the floor – tears began do roll down his cheeks."

"Dr. Caraway, I'm sorry for what I did, and I'll tell you right now – I'll never do it again. "

"Tell us about what you did, Phil."

Phil began to explain how he had become "hooked" on pornography through magazines and how he had begun to use the internet. It all started at home, and it just got out of hand. When asked why he started to do this at work, he replied that his life had become dull, even with the pornography on his home computer and getting the stuff through the filter. It was at first a challenge, and then he had needed a new challenge. That's when he decided to use Mr. Mitchell's computer.

"Phil, I'm truly sorry for your problem. You need to get professional help, and there are places, such as Region IV (Mental Health Department), that you can call on to begin the process of getting your life back."

“Dr. Caraway, am I going to lose my job?”

“Yes, Phil, your employment is being terminated today. If you had not set up the wire fraud to put blame on an innocent party, I might have been able to work something out, with a condition of rehab. However, that little trick you pulled sealed the deal – you proved that you cannot be trusted, and of course that’s crucial for a computer technician who has access to the entire campus. There’s also the matter of wire fraud. What you’ve done is illegal, as well as unethical and unprofessional. We’re considering whether to press charges on that.”

“I’m sorry I betrayed your trust and confidence, Dr. Caraway, and I’m sorry I’m losing the best job I could ever want to have at a college anywhere. I really blew it.”

“Yes you did. Phil, you are a young man, and you have a lot of years ahead of you. You are obviously a very smart and talented technician. This isn’t the end for you – it’s the beginning actually, because you can get help and start a new life that you can be proud of – life is about choices, and you’ve made some really bad ones. You have to face the consequences for those bad choices. But now you have a chance to make a new choice - take the high road to a successful treatment plan and then go back to work doing what you do best! Or...., you can continue down the road of bad choices and drown yourself in self pity and be a casualty. Find the truth for your life and move forward – you’ve got a lot of years ahead of you.

Phil, Barry will collect your keys and whatever else you may have that belongs to the college. He will accompany you, along with Chief Howard, to collect your personal things from your office.

One more thing, Phil, who’s Wendy?”

"Sir? Oh, you mean the emails. I really don't know. I've only been emailing her for a few weeks. We've never met, but she was one cool chick!"

"Ok. Do you know where she was when she was emailing you?"

"No sir. I think she may live in New Orleans."

"Why's that?"

"Well, just from the way she talked, ah, emailed."

"Ok, any questions, Phil?"

"No sir. Dr. Caraway, I plan to make something of myself, and when I do, I'll be back to apply for whatever position you have open in the Technology Department."

"Phil, I hope so. Good bye."

Phil and Barry left to collect Phil's personal things from his office.

When they had gone, Caraway and John Ford just looked at each other and shook their heads.

"John, do you really think Phil doesn't know who Wendy is?"

"I *really* don't think he does. I thought you might tell him."

"I started to, but I learned awhile back if there's no real purpose in telling someone something, why do it. He's got enough problems without carrying that around his neck – let him think she's some 'cool chick' in New Orleans.

I'll let you and Dr. Sutton handle Darlene."

"Yes sir. Of course, I've got it covered. We won't need her services any more.

Dr. Caraway, I wasn't sure where you were going with Phil at first, but let me tell you, if that kid ever makes something of himself, he owes it to you. You've thrown up the wall to stop his nonsense; you've given him the sermon he needs; and you've given him hope."

"Hope?"

"Yep. He just might show back up here one day a different man. You didn't rule out the possibility of a position. Would you give him one?"

"Like you said, I'm not ruling it out, but he's got a long way to go. Let's just hope he can get the help he needs."

Switching gears, Caraway commented, "I see the interviews are set up for Thursday on the Assistant Career Tech Dean's position."

"Yes sir. I think we'll be able to close the book on that one on Friday and have a recommendation for the Board for the following Tuesday. Of course we won't have the recommendation ready for you to send out to the Board in advance, but we'll be okay for Tuesday's Board meeting."

Caraway responded, "That's the best we can do under the circumstances. It'll be fine, sometimes personnel issues run close like that. I'll give Mr. Logan (Thomas Logan is chairman of the Board's Personnel Committee) a call and give him a heads up on this item."

They were interrupted when Judy buzzed to let Caraway know Dr. Summerset was in the outer office. Did he have time to see him for a few moments?

"Yes, Judy. We're done – I'll be right out. Judy, hold my calls while he's in my office please."

Ford excused himself to go back to his office to prepare for a meeting.

Summerset came in with a smile on his face – it was apparent he had some good news - at least Caraway hoped so!

"Robert, tell me about that smile – is that a sign of good news?"

"Yes sir, it is."

"Tell me about it."

"Well, first I checked to see who had a taser at the game Saturday – Chief Howard and Officer Sessions had one; then I found that two sheriff's deputies had one as well. I asked Chief Howard if there was a way to determine if a taser had been used, you know, like a gun when you shoot it. When you shoot a gun there's a smell for a while and other things you can look at. Well, I thought there should be a way to see if a taser had been used."

Caraway couldn't help but smile at Summerset's analogy.

Summerset continued, "The Chief said yes, there was, but he'd have to get the Sheriff's Department to make that determination for the Campus PD as well as the Sheriff Department's tasers. They have a special piece of equipment that will do that. He wasn't too optimistic about getting that information today, but when I told him we really needed it, he said he'd call Billy Newsome (Batson County Sheriff) himself and see if he could get it. He did, and he even got the printout for our officers and for each deputy that was at the game. They show beyond a doubt that their tasers were not used – the dates used were shown for each taser, and there were none used during that time frame."

Summerset handed Caraway a file that had the records for all four tasers in it, just to have for his records. In addition, there was a signed statement from Sheriff Newsome as to the authenticity of the records.

"Dr. Caraway, I think you probably owe the Sheriff a big one for this. According to the Chief, it was very unusual for him to be able to get this that quick. Not only that, the two deputies were not too happy about being questioned about their tasers – they felt their word should suffice. The Sheriff went beyond the call of duty – The Chief and Newsome are pretty tight, and I think the Chief leaned on him pretty hard because he knew how much you needed this information."

"Okay, so we now know for an absolute certain that no taser was used during the time of the game?"

"Yes sir."

"Good job, Robert. Please tell the Chief I appreciate it very much. Oh, and tell him I'll take Billy Newsome to lunch real soon."

"Yes sir. Just so you know and have this for your records too, I checked with people in the vicinity of the incident about whether anyone saw a taser used at the game. All negative – nobody saw a taser used at all."

"Good job on this report, Robert. It will certainly make the rest of my day go better! Have a good afternoon Robert. Oh, how's Hulk Berryman doing?"

"Dr. Caraway, he's doing really well. I'm so embarrassed that I let everything get out of hand so much in my division. You won't have to worry about that from now on. I'm on track, and Berryman is too."

"Good. Let me know if I can help with anything."

"Yes sir."

Caraway called Robert Case to give him the news about the taser. He hoped his report would satisfy him and his constituent; however, he had dealt with parents who thought their child had been mistreated before, and he knew it could still be an issue to deal with.

"Mr. Case, I'm following up on your call of this morning about Mr. Devlin's son."

"Oh, yes sir. I appreciate you calling me back. What did you find out about who used the taser?"

"Mr. Case, My VP for Student Services and the Chief of Campus PD have done a very thorough investigation and have found that no taser was used by our PD or by any other law enforcement officers at the ballgame that night."

"Really, are you sure?"

"Yes sir, we are absolutely sure. As a matter of fact, I have a certified statement by Sheriff Newsome to that effect."

"Well, I'll pass that information on to Bob (Devlin). He probably won't be happy. I think he wanted someone to be disciplined over this, and I don't think he planned for that to be his son. I guess he'll just have to take this up with his son."

"Mr. Case, when you talk with Mr. Devlin, tell him to call me if he wants to discuss this further."

"I'll do that. You have a good afternoon!"

"You too!"

Caraway wasn't sure how Mr. Devlin would react, but he felt really good that he had some documents that proved his case.

About an hour later Judy buzzed Caraway to let him know that Mr. Devlin was in the outer office and wanted to see him. Judy knew enough about the situation that she called Chief Howard as soon as Devlin went into Caraway's office. When she told the Chief about the situation, it took him less than five minutes to be in the hallway just outside the door.

"Come in Mr. Devlin. I assume you're here to talk to me about the question you had about a taser being used at the ballgame Saturday night."

"Yes sir, I am. My boy showed me a spot on his right thigh where he'd been shot with a taser. I understand from Robert Case now that you're denying a taser was used. I want some satisfaction, and I'm gonna get it from somebody."

"Mr. Devlin, I'm sorry about the wound you son has on his thigh, but it was not caused by a taser on Saturday night by any of our officers at the ballgame. Let me tell you what I've done to investigate this situation and then you can ask me any questions you want."

"Oh, I can't wait to hear what you've got to say to cover up the taser being used on my son."

"Mr. Devlin, just listen to what I have to say; then we can discuss anything about it you wish."

"Okay, let's hear it."

Caraway told him about the fact that Summerset had checked everyone who had been in the vicinity to see if anyone saw a taser being used and the fact that he found no one had seen a taser used or even out of the holster. Then he laid a copy of the taser records on his desk and told Mr. Devlin what they were and to take a look at them.

Mr. Devlin was not an educated man; he only finished the tenth grade years ago and had done manual labor all his life, but he had a bushel full of common sense. He was a man who respected authority, but he was also a man who did not stand for an injustice that he thought had been done to him or his family. He was a strict father and expected his children to do right by others, and he would not stand for them to be wronged by school officials or anyone else.

Today was a big test for Mr. Devlin. When he came into Caraway's office he was sure his son was tased, but now that he saw these documents he wasn't so sure. What he was looking at was actual records of taser usage, along with a certified copy of a Sheriff's statement, to the effect that no taser had been used period. He didn't have a clue as to what the records said, but he could read well enough to know what the sheriff said. He knew Sheriff Newsome and had a lot of respect for him – he wouldn't lie.

"Mr. Devlin, are you okay?"

"Yeah, I'm fine. I just don't know what to think – what's going on?"

"Mr. Devlin, have you talked with your son about Saturday night?"

"What do you mean? Of course, that's how I found out about the taser....I mean what I thought was a taser anyway. He told me about it."

"But, Mr. Devlin, have you really *talked* with him? Do you know any reason he would lie about this?"

"My son knows better than to lie to me! He knows he'll get a whooping like he's never got before."

Devlin's words implied he was fighting mad, but his voice cracked, and Caraway knew he was really more hurt and embarrassed than anything else – his son had lied to him, and he now knew it.

"Mr. Devlin, if I can make a suggestion, sit down and talk with your son – he has some reason for doing this – he may have been tased somewhere else and don't want you to know, or maybe it's some other kind of wound. I think if you will go to him and let him know that you know there was no taser, then maybe he'll open up and tell you what happened."

"Mr. (Dr.) Caraway, I appreciate your time and the trouble you've gone to today. I will handle my son in my own way. I'll be going now."

"Mr. Devlin, let me know if I can help you in any way."

There was no response as Devlin left the office.

As Mr. Devlin left the office, Chief Howard looked around the doorway at Caraway. "Are you okay Dr. Caraway?"

"Chief, are you here to watch my backside? Come on in."

The two of them talked about Devlin's reaction to the sheriff's statement and the copies of tapes from the tasers. Caraway told the Chief he was a little concerned about the boy's safety – he hoped Devlin would follow his advice, but his parting statement indicated otherwise. He asked Chief Howard if he would mind checking on the boy to see if he was in class tomorrow. The Chief suggested that since Devlin knew Sheriff Newsome pretty well and since the Sheriff was somewhat involved through the taser records, well, maybe Newsome could drop by the Devlin place just to visit – while there he could make some type of assessment as to how the boy was doing.

"Let's not overdo it Chief. I just don't want to fail to take precautions where they are appropriate. "

"I got it, Doc. I'll handle it - discretely."

"Discretely. Okay, Chief - thanks for showing up – I assume Judy called you as soon as Devlin came in my office."

"Now *she's* the one who looks out for your backside!"

"Oh, I know that very well."

"See you, Dr. Caraway."

"Have a good evening, Chief!"

Caraway had had a long day – it had been "Monday" all day long! The week had to get better. He headed home.

When Charles arrived home at six o'clock, Margie could tell he'd had a long day – he looked tired. She also knew he needed to share his day, but that he'd be short on detail. She put on her listening hat and asked him to "tell me about your day."

"Well, it's been a pretty unusual day. I got a call early this morning from Robert Case, you remember, Board of Supervisors in Batson County. He had been contacted by Bob Devlin, one of his constituents about his son being tased at the ball game on Saturday night."

"What? Tased? Did that really happen?"

"Well, no, thank goodness it didn't happen, but you know how it is, we had to investigate the complaint. It took the better part of the day dealing with that, but we have rock solid proof that it didn't happen. But, after I told Mr. Case and he referred my response to Mr. Devlin, Mr. Devlin actually came to see me at the office. I know you don't want to hear all the details, but the bottom line is that Bob Devlin's son lied about the taser, and now Devlin knows it. He finally accepted the proof and went home. I don't know what he'll do to his son, but I'm a little concerned for him.

I also met with Phil turner today."

Caraway told her the basics of what had happened with the violation of the computer network by Turner and that he had had to let him go as an employee.

"My goodness, Charles, you must be exhausted after all that!"

"I'm fine. I'm pleased to have closed the book on a couple of situations which could have been major problems for us."

"How about next week's Board meeting? Are you ready?"

"You're thinking about the issue that John Casco may bring up about the athletic facility."

"Of course, what else!"

"Well, we'll just see. I have confidence that we can show why we don't need to spend money from the reserve fund right now, but I also have confidence that Dr. Carson will handle the meeting very well. I think in the end, it will all work out fine."

"Charles, I think someone who could not remain calm and collected like you would have a problem being a college president. There are just too many issues you have to deal with – if you got upset about half of them, I'd probably be a nervous wreck myself."

"Good, I'm glad you're not letting this get to you. I'll try to remember to stay calm."

Charles enjoyed a slight chuckle as he was thinking – *I'm glad I don't tell you everything that happens!*

Tuesday and Wednesday were quiet except for the planning and preparation required for the monthly Board meeting. Caraway always had Judy send out an agenda for the meeting one week in advance. He also had her send out pertinent information with the agenda for any items which would require Board approval so the Board members could see that material in advance. He had found that Board members appreciated getting this information in advance and that it saved time at the meeting since they were more familiar with those items.

He was glad he had gotten closure on several items before this week so he could concentrate on the upcoming Board meeting. However, one important item did require his attention, the person to be recommended for the Assistant Dean of Career Technical Instruction. Judy had scheduled the three finalists for this Thursday. He and John Ford would interview them as a team. That would not only save time, but sometimes was more effective in making the best choice.

Caraway and Ford spent the morning on Thursday interviewing the three top applicants. After lunch they decided to go to the conference room next door and tell their secretaries to protect them from calls and visitors. Ford had shared the information he'd put together from his reference checks prior to the interviews. They'd spent about forty-five minutes actually interviewing each of the finalists. They had worked together before, so they had a plan about the questions to ask each of the applicants, and they knew the areas which needed explanation for a couple of the applicants.

Caraway began the meeting, "Well John, what you think? "

"Dr. Caraway, I think we have two applicants, Benjamin Brown and Mack Saunders, who could do the job. The third applicant, Mr. Carl Woods who was the committee's recommendation by the way, is not in the hunt as far as I'm concerned. What's your take?"

Caraway responded, "We've worked together too long – I totally agree with you. And don't forget Dr. Dupree had recommended Mack Saunders for the position. Do you have a personal preference, John?"

"I'm good with Saunders. There were things about both Brown and Saunders that I liked. I think either one would be fine, but in the end I think I would agree with Dr. Dupree. Saunders is a strong candidate. How about you?"

"I agree. You did a good job on the reference checks, by the way. It's amazing how many people don't do an adequate background check. Just think, we wouldn't have known about the interpersonal problems Mr. Woods had with a few of the teachers at Cascade High if you'd just stopped with the names he gave you on the reference sheet. How did you get onto that anyway?"

"Well, actually something his supervisor said tickled my curiosity, and I just followed up with a couple of teachers."

"Would he be a viable applicant if you hadn't found that little flaw?"

"I really don't think so. I wasn't really pleased with his interview. He seemed to say one thing with his mouth and something entirely different with his body language. I thought he seemed a little cocky in the interview. His paperwork looks pretty good actually, but that's about it. I think his references that were listed may have been somewhat political."

"Again, I agree. Okay, John, you meet with Dr. Dupree and tell her what you're going to recommend and then get something to me by tomorrow so we can close this out this week. Do you plan to handle the Committee, or are you going to let Dr. Dupree do that?"

"I think I'll let her handle the Committee. What do you think about her talking to each of the committee members separately? I'd like to close that loop, and to be honest, I'd like to know if there was any undue influence along the way. Mostly though, I want to be sure they see her as in charge here. Even though she came to us and had us to interview the applicants, she's still in charge."

Caraway liked Ford's idea, "That sounds fine, John."

Ford wanted a final okay from Caraway, "Are you sure you're ok with Saunders? "

"Sure, as long as you and Dr. Sutton are."

"Good! That's who we'll recommend to you tomorrow, officially."

"Okay, John, good job with this whole thing. I need to get some work finished before I go home. I'll see you at the game tonight. Are you and Vicki coming to the pre-game meal?"

"Yes sir, we'll see you there."

"Good!"

The Bulldogs played the Lions from Windsor Community College, a team that had been a challenge in some years, but which was having a tough season this year. The score was a lopsided 42 to 10. The stats for the game were more one-sided than the score. Coaches generally didn't like such a one-sided game, but this game did give one of the running backs a chance to gain much more yardage than usual, which consoled them a bit.

The president from Windsor wasn't able to attend the Thursday night game, so Charles and Margie just had a sandwich from the concession stand and visited with friends on the home side. As was usually the case, Charles saw several Board members. Nothing was said about the upcoming Board meeting next week.

Caraway spent some time Friday morning making the rounds out on campus just visiting with various groups, beginning at the maintenance facility at 6:30 AM and ending up in the computer center talking with Barry Smith and his staff about mid-morning.

When he got to the office he had the full file on the recommendation for the Assistant Career Tech Dean's position. He looked it over and decided that John had all the bases covered. Dr. Dupree would meet with the Committee today and close that loop before this final recommendation went to the Board on Tuesday. Caraway had no reason to think anything would go wrong at this point on the decision to employ Mack Saunders for the position.

Caraway knew that next week would be a long one with all that was on the schedule. The week of the regular monthly Board meeting was usually rather busy with preparations, and next week would be no exception. Caraway finished up in his office just after the lunch hour and decided to head into town for a late lunch at the local sandwich shop. Later he took time to visit with some of the community leaders, beginning with the Mayor. Those visits lasted until about four o'clock when it was time to head home for the weekend.

He knew these visits with local community leaders would be beneficial to the college down the road when they needed support from the community. As a matter of fact, the college and the community had a very good working relationship in many areas, partly due to such visits and the good will they brought. The college and the town shared resources when there was a need. One such area was the relationship between the local town police and the Campus Police. They were on the same radio frequency and were always ready to provide backup to each other whenever it was needed. They were working together now on crisis management for such things as an evacuation plan for the town and the college.

The weekend was quiet at home for Charles and Margie. They both had hobbies and things they loved to do to get work off their minds. Margie liked to sew and work in flower beds when weather permitted. This weekend was just perfect for that.

Charles had a small building out near the pond that was used for a boat house, but also for some wood working. He usually had a project that he was working on for Margie, but this weekend he piddled with his own projects. He had more equipment than he had room for in the twenty foot square structure, but he just made room as he needed it by moving equipment around. One of his favorite pieces of machinery was his lathe. He enjoyed turning pieces for various projects, but lately he had started making wooden bowls. He had no intention of selling his items in a flea market atmosphere, but he enjoyed giving them to friends, in this case Margie's friends.

Sunday was a pleasant day for Charles and Margie. After Sunday school and church they had one of Charles' favorite salads out on the patio. They both just relaxed with a good book in the afternoon.

Monday morning brought Caraway back to the reality of the job. He had enjoyed the weekend's relaxation, but he enjoyed the challenges of his job as well. He arrived in the office early on Monday. He was mentally alert after a weekend of rest. Monday passed quickly with the last minute preparation for the next day's meeting.

CHAPTER TWELVE

The day of the October Board meeting finally came. Caraway had in a strange way looked forward to this month's Board meeting. He wasn't at all sure how it would go, and whether he would end up with a Board directive to use part of the reserve fund to begin the process of building new athletic facilities, but he was ready to get it behind him. He had not been there when the new facilities had been proposed five years ago, but he certainly understood the need for them. The current facilities were adequate, barely in some cases, but he knew it was only a matter of time until something would have to be done to improve the existing facilities or build new ones. His only concern was that spending over one million dollars of reserve money could jeopardize the financial integrity of the college. He simply could not support that. He didn't know all the trustees that well yet, but he'd seen them make good decisions for two years now that were in the best interest of the institution. He had to trust the Board's collective wisdom and certainly their authority to provide policy and direction for the college.

Board Chairman Charles Carson called the meeting to order in the usual fashion. A prayer was said, and the Pledge of Allegiance was recited. Public prayer had begun to take on a new meaning for Caraway in light of the attack on public entities to stop having prayer and even reciting the Pledge of Allegiance. As Caraway thought about it, that was a fight he would probably have to make one day – they still opened public gatherings with prayer at Fair Oaks. He frankly was a little surprised someone hadn't complained already, but he knew it was only a matter of time.

Fourteen of the fifteen members of the Board were present. Caraway had been amazed when he first came to Mississippi that community college boards were large, and he was surprised at the very high rate of attendance by members of his Board. However he knew that his own Board was not the largest one. In discussions with his fellow presidents, he had discovered that other boards were as large as thirty members, and the high attendance was not at all unusual. He knew that individual board members were paid mileage and received a very nominal stipend of $40 per meeting, but they seemed glad to serve and dedicated to providing leadership for the college.

Minutes of the previous meeting had been sent out with the agenda for this meeting, so the usual motion was made, seconded and passed to approve them as distributed. The agenda included no item of business regarding the athletic facilities, so Caraway was prepared for someone, probably John Casco, to offer a motion to add that to the published agenda. He wasn't surprised when the motion was made by Casco, and the item was added to the end of the agenda without dissent. Discussion would be coming at the end of the meeting.

The various reports were heard, including the financial report. Joe Biggers didn't say anything about the extra information he had in his brief case. That would come when and if needed. There were a few items for approval under finance which went without a hitch. Joe always met with Dr. Caraway and Mr. Doug Bennett, Chairman of the Finance Committee, on any items which were unusual, so there were rarely any surprises at the Board meeting. This meeting was no exception so far.

Mr. Thomas Logan, Chairman of the Personnel Committee, handled the two personnel items on the agenda. The first item was to accept the resignation of Mr. George

Jacobson, upon his retirement. With a written recommendation by President Caraway in the Board files, Mr. Logan made a motion to accept the resignation. It passed unanimously. No details of complaints and meetings with the administration were mentioned. Mr. Logan was prepared to get the Board into Executive Session if questions had been asked that needed explanation, but that wasn't necessary.

The next personnel item was to consider the recommendation of President Caraway to employ Mr. Mack Saunders as Assistant Dean of Career Technical Instruction effective January 1 of the next year. Mr. Logan was also prepared to take the Board into Executive Session if the discussion became political. He had been fully briefed on the situation. When Mr. Logan called for discussion on his motion to approve the recommendation, Mr. Arnold Catledge asked, "Can you tell us about the application process for that job, and who were the finalists?"

Mr. Logan called on Dr. Ford to provide information about the finalists and the selection process. Dr. Caraway had assigned Dr. Ford to work with Mr. Logan on personnel issues and to be responsible for discussion of all personnel items at Board meetings.

Dr. Ford said, "There were fourteen applicants for this position. Six didn't meet the requirements for various reasons; five applicants were 'screened' by the committee, basically as the weaker candidates based on paperwork and reference checks; and three were interviewed.

The three finalists interviewed were Mr. Benjamin Brown, Mr. Carl Woods and Mr. Mack Saunders. The Committee made its recommendation to Dr. Dupree, Dean of Career Tech Instruction, and Dr. Dupree recommended Mr.

Saunders to me. I have to say that in light of the importance of this position, I personally did an extensive reference check on all three finalists; then, Dr. Caraway and I did a full interview with the three finalists. After the interviews by Dr. Caraway and me, we both agreed with Dr. Dupree's recommendation to employ Mr. Saunders. You now have Dr. Caraway's recommendation before you. I'll be glad to answer any other questions.

Mr. Catledge said, "I just wanted to know if Mr. Woods got a fair hearing. A friend of mine called and asked that I support him for the job. I explained that we had a process, but I'd check on it. I'm satisfied that the process was conducted in a professional manner. I have no further questions."

No other questions were asked, and the motion to accept President Caraway's recommendation passed on a voice vote without dissent.

Finally, the last item on the agenda was up for discussion. Caraway remained calm, but was also in a state of high alertness. He couldn't help but notice how calm Dr. Carson was when he called on John Casco to discuss his item of business. It was as if Carson knew how the discussion would go and the end result. But how could he?

"Mr. Casco, you're recognized."

"Thank you Mr. Chairman. Most of you remember that five years ago we discussed the need to build new athletic facilities on the home side of the football field. I know that a number of you attend games in the stadium, and you've seen for yourself that the concession area is unsightly and always in need of repair, and the press box has very limited space. That has become a greater problem in recent years, even during the last five years, because of the filming and video streaming that our PR department does for all home games. People can actually watch our team play from home through their computer because of this new feature. Anyway, the space in the press box is totally inadequate to allow people who need to be there to be accommodated. The restroom facilities are absolutely deplorable on the home side, as well as the visitor's side of the stadium. And it would be nice to have an area to invite our special guests to watch the game. President Caraway has no place to invite the visiting president to come to watch the game and perhaps have some refreshments during the game."

Casco continued, "I've talked to a number of you over the past couple of months, and I think almost all if not all of you agree that we need to solve this problem. Some of you have expressed concerns about, 'well, where is the money coming from to do this?' I know those concerns are out there; however, if we wait until we have that kind of money in hand, we may never get this done. There seems to always be another project that takes priority over this one. "

Caraway was paying close attention to the demeanor of Board members; he was very interested in getting a feel for how much support John Casco would have. He noticed that several were unconsciously shaking their heads no, while there were some heads nodding a sign of yes, we need to do this.

Doug Bennett, a banker from a nearby town who served as Finance Chair of the Board, interrupted Casco and asked what he thought the cost of this project would be.

Casco answered that the cost estimates were about $1 million five years ago. He indicated that this amount was still probably in the ball park, although it would be maybe 10% more today.

Miss Eleanor Montrose asked Chairman Carson to be recognized.

"Go ahead, Miss Montrose."

"Mr. Casco, you mentioned that several Board members had asked where we would get the money. I was one of those who asked that question, and I'm still asking, 'where will we get the money to do this?' You told me in our conversation that there was a reserve fund at the college. I'd like to hear from Dr. Caraway and maybe Mr. Biggers about that reserve fund."

Actually, Miss Montrose knew exactly how much money was in the reserve fund and also what contingencies might require some of it over the next few years. She was simply getting the point out in the open for discussion; just maybe some of the Board members didn't remember the amount and perhaps didn't know why it was there.

Caraway took the lead and told Miss Montrose that the reserve fund had a total of just under $3.5 million.

She then asked, "What is needed in such a fund to cover things we don't expect and to be sure we have enough for payroll every month? I remember when we've had to borrow money in the months of November and December to cover payroll because we were waiting for some type of reimbursement from the State Board. How much do we really need in that fund on a continual basis?"

Caraway spoke up, "I'll let Joe Biggers answer that."

Joe was ready for the question, "Well, the $3.5 million is a little short of what is needed to have a somewhat comfortable reserve fund. Of course you mentioned the payroll situation. We don't have that problem now, but if we spent, say, $1.3 million then we would be mighty tight just to make payroll without any major repairs or other unexpected expenses. Payroll is in the $2 million range each month. We sometimes wait a couple of months for a reimbursement from the State Board, and that can cause a pretty tight squeeze during those months."

Miss Montrose came back with, "So, what you're saying, Mr. Biggers, is that we cannot afford to spend a million or so of reserve without risking another situation where we have to borrow money at a high rate of interest again."

"I can't speak for the interest, but in my opinion we'd very likely have to borrow money if we used $1 million of the reserve."

Doug Bennett cut into the conversation once again. "Mr. Chairman, if I might add a word."

"Go ahead, Mr. Bennett."

"Well, as Finance Chairman, I want to just add that I recall when the fund balance was very low. I also recall that when we had our budget planning meeting how tough it was to say 'no' to some things we really wanted to do. We vowed that if we could ever get out of such a mess, we'd never get back into a situation where we had to say 'no' to things which were really needed and have to borrow money to pay the bills, including payroll.

Mr. Casco makes a good point about the need for facilities. I recall we took a tour of the facilities on the home side of the stadium five years ago when we were looking at this project. It was bad then, and I know it's even worse now. In my opinion we need to develop a plan to do this project over a period of time. Let me ask John (Casco) if he would be happy with a plan to break the project into three or four parts and do them one at a time as we can afford."

Casco was anxious to make his next point, "Well, in theory that would be something to consider, but in practicality, it would really end up costing us probably an additional twenty-five percent - contractors like to do projects like this all at once, and when they have do them piecemeal, they have start-up costs each time they do a part of the project, and it just costs more. But let me ask this question. Say we decided to do this project in three parts, when would we do the first part? From what Mr. Biggers said, it doesn't sound like there's enough money to spend anything now. When would we see something built – just how long do we have to wait?"

Mr. Theodore "Ted" Watson asked to be recognized – and a hand also went up by Mrs. Betsy Waycaster.

The Board Chairman ruled, "You're recognized Mr. Watson, then Mrs. Waycaster is next."

"I just want to say that I think we're overlooking the importance of athletics at Fair Oaks. Look at the big picture. Sports are a big part of what we offer our students and our community. It's a good part of the community college culture!"

Watson pointed out, "Our enrollment wouldn't be near four thousand students if we didn't have athletics, and the income to the college would be minus the tuition for those athletes; we wouldn't have the federal Pell Grant money that most athletes bring with them, and we wouldn't have ticket sales. Has anybody ever done research to see how much money athletics brings in to the college? I think we need to look at those things – the big picture, if you will, - before we sell athletics short. One more thing, Mr.

Chairman, if I might; do we as Board members realize how much the good publicity we get through the athletic program helps the college? Our coaches have done a great job – we have a winning tradition in almost all major sports, especially in football. When you see a picture or an article on the front page of the *Batson Courier*, it's about athletics 90% of the time! Let's think about these things.

One more thing, have any of you talked with any of the coaches about this? How do they feel about being short changed on facilities? And if we have to cut more on the budget, are we going to cut their equipment next?"

Chairman Carson spoke up, "Mr. Watson, you've asked several questions, some of which you recall we discussed five years ago, but maybe we need to refresh our memories on now.

Mrs. Waycaster, I'll get to you, but I think we need to have a response to some of these questions. Mr. Watson has posed some serious issues we all need to reflect on today.

Dr. Caraway, how do you want to address these questions?"

"Thank you, Dr. Carson, you are absolutely right. These are very important questions which need to be answered. I'll just make a couple of comments and then ask Joe Biggers to address specifics. I believe he's in the best position to provide hard facts regarding the issues Mr. Watson has raised.

I want to thank Mr. Watson for his comments, and while I agree with his assessment of the importance athletics plays in the lives of our students, particularly the athletes, I have to say that the opportunities an educational institution offers must begin with the preparation of individuals to be good, knowledgeable citizens who can provide for their families and can contribute to the local economy. We must place our number one priority on providing those opportunities. And, I'd point out that Mr. Watson didn't even mention the discipline and character that student athletes gain on the practice field, as well as the playing field; I can't speak for some of the parents level of discipline and character (light laughter), but seriously, they should also be the beneficiary of these lessons learned by their sons and daughters.

The bottom line is that yes, absolutely, athletics are part of our culture in the community college family. However, we must be a viable and fiscally responsible institution to be able to have an athletic program in the first place."

With that, Caraway called on Joe Biggers to provide any information he thought might help answer Mr. Watson's questions.

Joe took his lead from what Dr. Caraway had said. He didn't need to hammer anyone too hard with the hard cold facts, but he had a chance to shore up the more emotional "mission" side of the argument with some solid facts. He needed to do that with some delicacy so as not to provoke anyone who might want to defend their argument about the importance of athletics.

Joe began with, "Ladies and gentlemen, Dr. Caraway and I have had discussions on some of these very points, and I was here five years ago when we looked at this issue. In addition, years ago the college president was asked in a faculty meeting why we spent so much money on athletics – I suspect their motive in asking this question was somewhat different than our motive today.

So, we've looked at this issue pretty closely over the years. I'm a numbers guy, so I don't feel real comfortable not quoting the exact facts to you today (actually he could have provided some very hard cold facts), but I do remember the major points of analysis. I'll just lay out a few of those for you. First, an institution does spend money on athletics – it is a net expense. After you take into account the income from student tuition and federal grants money, there is a net cost for athletic programs.

Second, there's a common misunderstanding about gate receipts at ballgames. People think we make money at the gate. The fact is that Dr. Caraway, as does every other president in the state/country, sends out athletic passes to supporters of the college each year. To name a few, you as Board members get a pass, all full time faculty and staff get a pass, students pay a nominal amount, parents of athletes get a pass, all mayors and members of the Boards of Alderman in surrounding towns get a pass, and the list goes on. You may ask why we don't charge members of these groups at the gate. Which group would you not give a pass to?"

Mr. Troy Montgomery spoke up and said, "We can give up our pass, and then maybe that'll set an example for other groups to follow."

Mr. Buddy Avery immediately chimed in with, "Speak for yourself, Troy, but I want my pass. I enjoy going to our games."

Dr. Carson used the gavel to call for order and asked Joe Biggers to continue.

"Basically, all of these groups provide some type support for the college. This is just Dr. Caraway's way of saying on behalf of the college that we appreciate their support.

Income from concessions goes to the local Lions Club to help fund community service projects. There's another group that supports the college, and by the way, those who work in the concession stand get into the games without charge.

And I didn't mention that officials at other schools have their own State MACJC passes to attend athletic events statewide. These are of course honored at our events. The bottom line is that it doesn't take long to count the money taken up at the gate."

Joe continued, "And finally, the issue about athletes bringing Pell Grant money with them to the college has been discussed for years. I won't attempt to argue the point, but honestly, I could probably prove that this provides a significant net income to the college – that it overcomes the expense side of the ledger" (there was a noticeable reaction by Casco, Watson, and several other board members).

Then Joe said, "I could just as easily prove that it's a negative – an expense. It depends on how you look at the numbers, and it depends somewhat on speculation – how many athletes would have come anyway, how many other students did they bring with them, et cetera. This is an age old question; one that I suspect will be discussed from now on. The point I'd make is that you simply cannot isolate all the variables to determine the athletic cost/benefit issue."

Joe looked at Dr. Caraway and said if there were specific questions, he'd be happy to address them.

Caraway was very pleased with his VP for Finance. He and Joe had looked at the numbers before the meeting and had decided that he would simply try to get a feel about the need for actual statistics and use his discretion about whether to use them. He had done a great job of reading the Board, and had used that to his advantage. He paused for reaction at the strategic places and had driven his points home like a champ. Caraway's pride in Joe showed on his face for those who were paying attention.

Caraway looked at Carson for his signal. Then he followed up on Joe's comments and finished driving home the point he had made about priorities, "We are indeed a community college – we provide for many aspects of life for our students – athletics is, is of course, a major aspect. However, there are others, for example, we offer a Community Arts Series, where we feature international performing artists, as well as local talent; and we provide a community service function for our senior adults which includes travel experiences as well as educational experiences. Last year alone we taught over seventy-five special classes to over twelve hundred people in our community.

There are just a lot of things we do as a college, but I must say again that our main objective is to provide access to 'opportunity' for people to gain whatever kind of educational benefit they wish right here."

When Caraway had finished his comments, Dr. Lester Price, a local dentist, raised his hand for recognition. Dr. Carson said, "Dr. Price, you'll be recognized as soon as Mrs. Waycaster has her say. Mrs. Waycaster, sorry you had to wait so long, but you now have the floor."

"Thank you, Mr. Chairman. Our President has spoken so eloquently in addressing our priorities and the real issues we should be concerned with today, I wouldn't dare try to improve on his words – he took the words 'right out of my mouth,' as they say. But he made them sound so much better than I ever could have."

Light laughter and applause.

Chairman Carson called on Dr. Price. Dr. Price was an elderly gentleman who was usually pretty quiet at Board meetings unless a major issue was discussed. He was a very perceptive man and often heard what others did not. He had been quiet so far at this meeting, but he took advantage of this opportunity to get a clarification.

"Mr. Chairman, a few moments ago Ted Watson made a comment that I'd like to follow up on. Ted, you asked if any of us had heard from the coaches. I was just curious if any of us had heard from the coaches."

Pause – silence.

Price continued, "How about you Ted? Have you?

Ted looked a bit nervous and almost imperceptibly glanced over at John Casco before he spoke. Caraway was zeroed in on Watson and noticed both him and Casco. He also caught the very, very slight nod "no" by Casco.

Ted answered by saying, "Actually, I haven't. I just wondered if the administration had heard anything from them."

Caraway distinctly remembered that Watson had directed his question to the Board, not the administration.

Dr. Price looked at Dr. Caraway and asked, "Dr. Caraway, have you heard from the coaches?"

Caraway answered by saying, "No I haven't; I think they've been too busy winning ball games!"

There was laughter.

Lester Price may or may not have seen what Caraway saw, but it was as if he smelled blood – John Casco's!

"John, how about you? You've been quiet since you started this discussion – I know it's gone pretty fast, and you've not had a chance to get a word in edgewise. Which coaches have you talked with regarding this issue?"

Caraway was thinking, oh, yeah, Dr. Price had caught the interchange of looks between Watson & Casco.

John Casco had to make a quick decision. The cat was "out of the bag", as the old saying goes! Casco had indeed been contacted by Coach Dawson, supposedly with Coach West's blessing, but he had given his word he would not divulge that conversation to anyone, let alone to the entire Board of Trustees. He had a choice – break the confidence of Coach Dawson, or tell a (little white?) lie and betray the trust of his fellow Board members. Or.....maybe he could just answer without telling the name of the coach – maybe that would do it.

After a pregnant pause, John answered, "Yes, as a matter of fact I have had some conversations with coaches. I really don't see the harm in a Board member talking with a coach or two about the athletic program. After all, they know we're interested in their program, and the fact is we do need to do something about the facilities.

John Casco felt the eyes of other Board members, but he didn't realize the several things that really drew their attention. First, he was sweating profusely; he paused a little too long; and he was entirely too defensive.

Dr. Price had the floor, so he saw no need to ask for recognition again; he just followed up with, "Well, John maybe you can tell us about those conversations. Did you say more than one conversation? I can't remember."

Casco finally faced the reality that he was not going to get off easy. He said, "Fellow Board members, I did talk with one of the football coaches, who I think was speaking for all of them actually. However, he didn't want to get involved, so he actually talked with me in the strictest of confidence. I don't think it's really relevant who the coach was, and I will not dishonor that conversation by breaking that confidence."

Dr. Price spoke up and asked, "If you can't tell us who the coach was, and I respect that by the way, maybe you can tell us what he had to say."

"Well, he just mentioned that he thought the college hadn't put enough emphasis on the upgrading of athletic facilities since he'd been here. He thought the college needed to recognize the importance of having nice facilities at least on the home side of the stadium, especially since the team had a winning tradition."

Dr. Carson was keenly aware of the demeanor of the Board members – John Casco was embarrassed, and his fellow Board members were embarrassed for him. In fact, he had been a solid Board member through the years, and he seemed to be somewhat out of character today. Carson called a short recess with the hope that everyone could regain their composure.

"The hour is getting late – we've been here a little longer than usual already, but I think we need to discuss this just a bit more – let's take a fifteen minute break."

During the recess Caraway mouthed "good job" to Joe Biggers and gave him the universal sign to call the cafeteria to let them know they would be about thirty to forty-five minutes late for dinner.

John Ford briefly spoke to Caraway as the break began, "Dr. Caraway, you and Joe make a good team. This meeting could have gotten out of hand, had it not been for your delicate handling of the situation."

"Well, John, Dr. Carson really is the one who's kept the meeting in balance. He was very wise just now to call for a recess."

"You're right, of course, but you've all handled a potentially volatile situation very well."

Caraway had gotten to know the Board Chair pretty well in the short two and a half years he'd been here. He was somewhat curious as to how he would proceed after the break. He was thinking of what he would do were he in Dr. Carson's shoes and decided he'd appoint a small committee to bring some recommendations back to the full Board. He would be sure to put John Casco on the committee, but also make sure the committee would have some strong leadership.

The recess went by quickly - Dr. Carson gaveled the Board to order.

"We've been here a long time, and we've made some very good points on both sides of this issue. I think we owe it to ourselves, but mostly to this college, to make the best decision possible. This discussion deserves some very serious consideration, so unless there's objection, here's what I'm gonna do (everyone was interested in hearing the "plan", but no one was interested in objecting to it whatever it might be!). I'm appointing a committee of three people to work with Dr. Caraway to develop a plan for the construction of the athletic facilities on the home side of the stadium."

Dr. Carson continued, "Mrs. Waycaster, I would like you to chair that committee. Doug Bennett and John Casco, I'd like you to serve on the committee. Is there any one of you who feels like you can't serve on the committee?"

No response.

"Good. Now I'd like this Board to set one parameter that we will consider sacrosanct – that is that we will have a fund balance of 'X' number of dollars for emergencies and obligations that we will not touch for anything that's not absolutely necessary. In other words, we must have this amount in reserve before we can budget any further expenses for the athletic complex.

Do I hear a motion as to the amount that needs to be in that fund?"

Several Board members turned toward Doug Bennett, Finance Chairman. He was the one they usually looked to for direction on financial issues. He was a solid Board member!

Bennett looked at Joe Biggers briefly as if they'd already talked (maybe they had). Bennett made a motion that the reserve fund be protected at the level of $4 million.

Mrs. Montrose seconded the motion.

Mr. Casco offered a motion to amend Mr. Bennett's motion to adjust the amount to $3.8 million arguing that it could be a priority of the Board to increase that over the next few years. His motion was seconded by Ted Watson.

The "question" was called on the motion to amend – it failed by a vote of five yeas and nine nays. Dr. Carson did not vote, as was his custom – except in very unusual circumstances, he only voted to break a tie vote.

Michael Bishop, who had been exceptionally quiet during the entire discussion, called the "question" on the original motion by Doug Bennett. The motion passed by a voice vote without opposition; however, Caraway noticed that Casco, Watson and a couple of other Board members did not vote. There would be some repair work to be done, but Dr. Carson had set the stage for that to begin by putting Casco on the committee.

The Board concluded its business in short order after this issue was handled, and made its way to the meal in the private dining room of the cafeteria.

Following dinner, Dr. Carson spoke to Caraway briefly, "Charles, let's have coffee in the morning. What time do you usually get out?"

"Dr. Carson, I'm an 'early bird', whatever's good for you."

"Well, why don't we meet down at the *Coffee Bean* around 6:30?"

"That's fine. I'll see you there. Have a good night."

"You too!"

Charles had to be pleased with the Board meeting. The Board, under Dr. Carson's leadership, had set a very practical plan in place to satisfy those who wanted new/improved athletic facilities as well as those who wanted to protect the fiscal integrity of the college.

Caraway got home a little later than usual from the Board meeting, and Margie was anxious to hear what had happened.

"Charles, tell me about the Board meeting. I can't wait to hear!"

"Well, it's really a rather long story, but the bottom line is that Dr. Carson appointed a three person committee to work with the administration to develop a plan to build the facilities; but more importantly they set a minimum of $4 million to have in the reserve fund that cannot be touched for this or any other project."

Margie asked, "Who's on the committee?"

"Betsy Waycaster will chair the committee, and Doug Bennett and John Casco are the other two members."

"John Casco is on the committee?"

"Oh, yeah, and that's really the best part. Both sides of the issue are represented on the committee, and these are really good people who have the best interest of the college at heart, even John Casco. He's just a little anxious about the athletic facilities. He's a good strong supporter of the college."

"Charles, can't you get special building funds from the state – bond money?"

"Well, yes, but it has been really hard to get any appreciable amount in recent years because of the state budget crisis. The Legislature has been reluctant to pass bond bills, and the Governor just hasn't been willing to allow that kind of money, except for emergencies. But if we do get bond money, the first $1.3 million or so will be designated for this project."

"Are you okay with that?"

"Sure, we do have a need there, and the Board has now put a priority on that project."

"So, all in all you had a pretty good meeting."

"Yes, we did. But, you know, I feel very fortunate to have Dr. Carson as Board Chairman. He really did a superb job of conducting that meeting today."

"So, what do you think the committee will do?"

"I'm not sure what kind of plan will be developed, but I think the committee will proceed with due caution. I look forward to working with them to develop a plan."

"Good, sounds like things did go rather well."

What Charles didn't tell Margie was that he had some business to discuss with Coach West, head football coach.

CHAPTER THIRTEEN

Caraway met Dr. Carson for coffee as prearranged on Wednesday morning.

"Good morning Charles! And how did you sleep last night?"

Caraway couldn't help but notice the cheerful mood Dr. Carson was in this morning. He definitely thought the previous day's meeting had been a victory for the "good guys."

"Dr. Carson, I have a built-in personal policy that I don't let my work get in the way of sleep. But I have to tell you, when I can't figure out something, it sometimes keeps me awake."

"And what is it you can't figure out? I assume you didn't sleep well last night, after we had such a good meeting."

"I'm afraid you assume correctly. What I can't quite figure out is how you knew how that meeting would go. I know you've been on the Board for a long time and actually chairman for a long time, but how could you know how that meeting would turn out? Can you share that with me?"

"Charles, when you've been around as long as I have, you just know. But I will share one thing that you must keep in confidence, at least for now."

"Of course!"

"I sometimes have an ace up my sleeve. In this case I had an ace, maybe two, but one for sure. You see, I reviewed my copy of the Board By-Laws prior to the meeting just to be sure, but we have a long standing policy that if an item that carries an expense of $1 million or more is tabled, then it takes a two thirds vote plus one to bring that item off the table."

"I don't quite understand. That wasn't mentioned at the meeting, and we did discuss the tabled item."

"Ah hah, that's the very point. We discussed a *new* item that John Casco placed on the agenda, but there was never a motion to build the facility."

"I'm still confused. What if there had been a motion to build?"

"Then I would have called a 'point of order' and referred back to the fact that we tabled that item five years ago and that it couldn't be voted on as a new item but only as a tabled item brought back up for consideration."

"In that case, how can we ever get it off the table without two-thirds (plus one) vote?"

"Well, actually, the tabled motion dies if not revived within a five year period. So, it's there until the end of five years; what we *can do* is develop a plan for which we can get the eleven members' (two-thirds plus one) support."

"In other words we've got to reduce the price to less than $1 million as a new item, or we have to have eleven votes to approve building the facility."

"Yes, that's the short of it."

"Do you think any of the other Board members know or remember that policy?"

"Well, maybe one or two. They were professional enough to let the discussion proceed without bringing a parliamentary question into play."

"And I guess Leon Burchfield knew as well?"

"Yes, of course! I called him just to be sure. By the way, he said you'd already given him a heads-up, so I thought you might know until just now."

Caraway laughed, "Oh no, I didn't have a clue. But I did know that there could be plenty of parliamentary questions at the meeting."

"You're very intuitive, Charles. You're a good President, one this institution needs. I hope you will stay at Fair Oaks a long time."

"Thank you, sir. I have to return the compliment and say that I hope you stay on the Board as Chairman as long as I'm President. By the way, can you tell me about your second ace?"

"Sure, it's another by-laws issue. We keep saying it's been five years since we tabled this issue, but that's not quite true. It won't be five years until next month's meeting. If we had not covered this item at this meeting and it had come up at next month's meeting, my first ace would have been trumped. You see, we also have a policy that if an item is tabled it will automatically be neutralized after five years.

Charles, you know you're really partly responsible for the way the meeting turned out. Your comments were short, but were very wise and persuasive. I watched the Board members' faces as you were speaking; they were greatly influenced by your comments. And, you set the stage for Joe Biggers' comments, which he delivered quite well, by the way. I assume he did have the numbers available, but chose not to hammer anyone at the meeting."

"Yes sir."

"I have a question, Charles. Do you know what's going on between Mr. Casco and the coach or coaches. John was quite nervous, and there's something that's not quite right."

"Yes sir. I think I do. I'll take care of that as soon as the season's over; I'll leave the detail of how that's handled up to Coach West." Caraway was thinking *Coach Dawson is young and still has a lot to learn. One of those things he'll learn is that you don't go to Board members with your problems or complaints.*

"You probably shouldn't give me any more detail at this point, but I'm glad you're on top of it."

"Yes sir."

"One more thing, Charles. Leon Burchfield keeps me informed on potential issues. He'd never betray your confidence, or mine, but remember that he represents the Board. He and I have an understanding that he'll always give me a heads-up on any matter that may impact the Board. He has not shared details with me at this point, but I know you're dealing with some tough issues. I want you to know that I know, but I also want you to know that I trust your judgment as much as anyone I've worked with in this job."

"I appreciate that sir. But I need to share with you that I have no secrets from you when it comes to this job. I'll provide as much detail as you want, but I will not make a practice of disturbing you with matters you're paying me to handle, unless I think it'll be a matter the Board will need to decide.

"I'm sure you'll provide the proper notification to me should the need arise."

"Yes sir."

"Charles, the coffee is on me. You have a good day at the office today and a good week. Don't hesitate to call me if you need anything."

"Thank you sir. I hope you have a good day as well."

That morning Judy had arrived to work at 7:45 and had gotten everything started for the day, including the pot of coffee that she knew Dr. Caraway would want to have waiting when he got there. He had sent her a quick text message to remind her that he was meeting with Dr. Carson and might be a little after eight o'clock getting to the office. As Caraway entered the office, Judy smiled and commended him on his presentation to the Board yesterday. She commented that it was obvious that they had a great deal of respect for him.

Caraway thanked her for the vote of confidence and said, "Don't forget about Joe (Biggers); he did an outstanding job of relating the real facts to the Board about the cost of athletic programs."

Caraway asked about messages and calls and found that the morning was going to be pretty light; it was Friday, and he had no appointments on the schedule for the day.

Caraway closed the door and enjoyed the peace and quiet in an easy chair over in the corner of his office. He was thinking about the trials and challenges of the past few weeks and how fortunate he was to have such a great team at Fair Oaks to help him get through the tough decisions that had to be made. From his Administrative Assistant who took care of him on a daily basis to the administrative team that did a super job of helping him solve problems, they all contributed to his success as President. He reminded himself that a good college president surrounds himself with top notch people who can be empowered and trusted to make decisions on a daily basis and who are there to help the leader make the really tough calls that sometimes have to be made. He couldn't have been more proud of his team over the past month!

Then Caraway thought about another team member, his wife Margie, who was always there by his side to listen and offer advice. The fact that Margie had such strong parents who had allowed her to learn the lessons of life as a young girl greatly contributed to her ability to look at things with calm resolve. He valued her advice greatly, but the fact that she loved and cared deeply for him gave him an inner strength that meant more than words could express.

As he reflected on the past challenges, he knew without doubt there'd be new challenges. But he felt a new strength to fight the challenges of tomorrow. As he thought about it, he was surrounded by people of great "strength" who were there to support him as the leader.

Bring on the new challenges!

STUDY GUIDE

STUDY GUIDE

The purpose of this Study Guide is to provide guidance to the student who wishes to use the scenarios in this story as a means of studying the decision-making process. The questions provided for the various major areas of decision-making by President Caraway and others are intended to stimulate an in-depth analysis of those decisions. Students are encouraged to critique the decisions and the rationale for making those decisions made by President Caraway and other college leaders in this story. They are also encouraged to develop their own responses to the situations presented.

Discussion leaders are encouraged to select the questions for group discussion according to major points they wish to make.

Since most of the scenarios are covered in more than one chapter in the book, the Study Guide is broken down into specific areas of decision-making rather than by chapter.

I. SEVEN SCENARIOS FOR DECISION-MAKING

A. Board issue to build athletic facilities

- From what you know from this story, do you think John Casco is a good Board member? Why? Why not? Cite facts to support your conclusion.

- When Mr. Casco was approached by an assistant football coach regarding football facilities, he decided to "drum up" support of his fellow Board members to build new athletic facilities. Was this an appropriate action? What other actions could/should he have taken?

- Was it appropriate for Mr. Casco to agree to keep the confidence of a football coach? Why? Why not?

- Was it appropriate for Michael Bishop to discuss the John Casco situation with President Caraway, or should he have first gone to the Chairman of the Board? Explain.

- Was the discussion between Michael Bishop and President Caraway appropriate? Why? Why not?

- Did President Caraway establish a "condition" to the confidentiality asked for by Michael Bishop at their meeting? If so, what was the condition?

- Was it appropriate for Pres. Caraway to meet with the Board Chairman to discuss the issue about athletic facilities? Why? Why not? If you had been

Caraway, what would you have done differently?

- Does President Caraway have a positive relationship with his Board of Trustees? If so, what evidence is there to support such a relationship?
- Was it appropriate for Dr. Carson not to mention to the Board that the motion (5 years ago) to build athletic facilities had been "tabled" and would require eleven (2/3 plus 1) votes to bring the issue off the table for a vote? Explain.
- Comment on Dr. Carson's actions at the Board meeting when he called a recess and provided an opportunity for everyone to settle down. What do you think his motive was for this action? Explain.
- Comment on Dr. Carson's action to appoint a committee and whom he appointed to serve on the committee to work with President Caraway regarding building athletic facilities. Can you think of a better solution?
- What action, if any, should President Caraway take regarding Coach "Mac" Dawson? Explain.

B. **Girl Dismissed From Dormitory**

- The Campus Police walked through the dormitory and looked in student living quarters ostensibly on a regular "room check" to look for signs of drugs. On information obtained through a confidential informant, they were specifically looking to see if Susie Jones had evidence of drugs in her room. Upon a visual search of her room they saw evidence of drugs in Susie's room. Was this a violation of search and seizure? Explain your answer.

- Once evidence of drugs was found in Susie's room on the weekend, was the warrant to go back to her room necessary or just prudent? Explain.

- What actions did President Caraway take after he received the phone call from Mr. Sistrunk? Were all of his actions appropriate? If not, explain. What actions would you have taken?

- When President Caraway found that the Student Services Division of the college had "dropped the ball," he met with Dr.

Summerset and Mr. Berryman. Evaluate his actions in that meeting. Was he too tough, not tough enough? Explain. What would you have done differently?

- Was President Caraway's contact with the college attorney, Mr. Burchfield, timely? Should he have called him sooner? Should he have waited until he had more information from Chief Howard? Discuss pros & cons of each choice.

- Should President Caraway have mentioned the potential lawsuit by Mr. Sistrunk to Dr. Carson, Board Chairman, when they met on Friday after Caraway had received the call from Mr. Sistrunk on Thursday? Why? Why not? Explain.

- Was it appropriate for President Caraway to have Chief Howard investigate the situation rather than delegate that to Dr. Summerset, Chief Howard's supervisor? Explain.

- Was it appropriate for President Caraway to have the college attorney work out a "deal" with Mr. Sistrunk? Should President Caraway have pushed the DA's office to prosecute Susie for dealing drugs? Why? Why not? Discuss.

- Was President Caraway's assignment for Summerset & Berryman and the follow-up meeting with them an effective means of handling their failure to properly handle the Susie Jones situation? What would you have done differently? Explain.

C. Computer Security Violation

- Since Phil Turner had no contractual status, what right of employment did he have? Did he have grounds for a lawsuit to regain his job? Explain.

- When President Caraway first heard that it was almost certain that Mr. Mitchell had violated computer security, was he justified in instructing Barry Smith to work long hours at college expense to rule out the 1% chance that someone else was using Mr. Mitchell's computer? What approach would you have taken in this situation? Why? Why not? Explain your answer.

- Was President Caraway overcautious in not letting Barry have help in finding the problem with the violation of computer security? Explain.

- When President Caraway met with Barry Smith and Phil Turner, was Caraway too tough on Phil? Not tough enough? Explain.

- If Barry had found evidence of "child pornography" in his search, what additional actions should President Caraway have taken? Explain.

- If Barry had found that "Wendy" had been a student at Fair Oaks, what consequences would Caraway have had to deal with in this situation? If that had been the case, should he have taken a different approach with Phil Turner? How would the end result have been different? Explain.

- Did Barry Smith violate anyone's privacy in placing hidden cameras in the workplace? The Computer Lab? Explain.

- Assuming Mr. Mitchell had not already been confronted with the issue of computer security, should he have been told about the violation of computer security involving his office computer after the truth was determined? Why? Why not?

D. The Valued Employee with a Questionable Past

- When Joe's friend Harry mentioned to President Caraway that Joe had made a mistake in his youth, Caraway reluctantly probed to determine more information about that mistake. Should he have been reluctant to probe? Was he justified to probe into Joe's past? Explain.

- Following President Caraway's meeting with Harry, were his actions appropriate? What would you have done differently?

- Did Joe "lie" when he completed his application? Explain.

- Caraway struggled with the question of whether he should approach Joe with the issue of his past. Would you have talked with Joe? If so, what would you have said? Discuss pros & cons.

- Should punitive action be taken against Joe? Explain.

E. Question Regarding Use of Taser at Ballgame

- Did President Caraway "give in to politics" by placing a priority on determining the facts in the "taser" situation? Explain.

- Do you think President Caraway would have handled the situation differently if Mr. Devlin had called him rather than Mr. Case? As president, what would you have done differently in this situation?

- Was it appropriate for Mr. Case to mention the county increase in budget for the college at the end of their conversation? Why? Why not?

- How well did President Caraway handle the meeting with Mr. Devlin? What would you have done differently?

- If an officer (Campus PD or Sheriff's Dept.) had used a taser on a student at the ballgame, would there have been a cause for a lawsuit against the college? Why? Why not? How would you have handled the situation if that had occurred?

F. The American National Government Instructor - George Jacobson

- How well did Mr. Butler handle the first complaints about Mr. Jacobson last spring? What would you have done differently?

- When students complained to Dr. Sutton about Jacobson in the fall, should she have sent the students to Mr. Butler, the Division Chair? Explain.

- How well did Dr. Sutton handle the meeting with Mr. Jacobson? What would you have done differently?

- When Mr. Jacobson appealed Dr. Sutton's decision to Dr. Ford, was it appropriate to have Dr. Sutton in the meeting? Was it a good practice to tape record the appeal by Jacobson? How well did Dr. Ford handle the meeting with Mr. Jacobson? What would you have done differently?

- Did Mr. Jacobson have a case against the college for retaliation? If so, on what grounds? Discuss.

- Were there grounds to dismiss Mr. Jacobson anywhere along the way, beginning with the student complaints in the spring? Is so, what were they?

- Was Mr. Jacobson "salvageable" as a full-time instructor? Explain.

- Was the end result in the "Jacobson" situation the best for the institution? Explain.

G. Assistant Dean Of Career Technical Instruction

- How well did the "Screening Committee" process work in making a selection to recommend a person for the position of Assistant Dean of Career Technical Instruction? What actions, if any, does the college administration need to take to strengthen the Screening Committee process?

- When the Screening Committee is 100% in favor of a candidate and the Dean (the person to whom the committee is to make a recommendation) is totally opposed to the committee's recommendation, what actions would you take if you were the Dean? Explain.

- Was Dr. Dupree's concern for the committee process versus hiring the "right person" for this position justified? Which is more important? Explain.

- Was Dr. Ford's action in going to Dr. Caraway with the decision-making process before making a recommendation appropriate? Explain.

- Was it appropriate for Dr. Ford and President Caraway to do a full interview with the top three applicants? Explain.

II GENERAL PERSONNEL ISSUES

A. Did President Caraway surround himself with "top notch" people? Explain your answer and provide examples.

B. Was President Caraway a "Level 5" leader? Explain your answer.

C. How well did Dr. Dupree, Dr. Sutton, & Dr. Ford carry out their responsibilities in the various situations in the story? Explain.

D. How effective was Dr. Carson as the Board President?

E. Characterize Mrs. Margie Caraway. How well did she live up to your expectations of a First Lady of a Community College?

F. Discuss the appropriateness of conversations between President Caraway and his wife "Marge". Was she a good "sounding board" for him? Did he tell her too much that was confidential? Explain.

III. GEMS AND TIPS FROM THE STORY.

A. Keep confidential personnel files in a very secure place.

B. Provide an opportunity for others to give you their ideas before you tell them yours.

C. Look for ways to "salvage" employees before giving up on them.

D. Employment Screening Committees should be given specific instructions and be given orientation on their responsibilities and authority in the hiring process.

E. Learn to trust your leaders.

F. The relationship between a college president and the chairman of the Board of Trustees is very important.

G. As a college president one should develop a close working relationship with the college attorney.

H. A college leader can learn a lot by visiting with staff on "their turf," especially early in the morning as they get the day started.

I. A college leader should be available to college personnel, both electronically and in person.

J. When speaking to civic groups, always find out the amount of time given for your speech and finish on the short side of that time, leaving time for questions if possible. NEVER go beyond the time allotted.

K. Make notes for a speaking engagement, make a short outline of those notes, be familiar with the outline; then put the outline in your pocket for reference if needed.

L. Make notes for the file (not official personnel file, but confidential file in most cases) after a meeting with an employee on a matter that may be controversial.

M. Tape conversations that represent an official complaint or an appeal. Make it clear to the person taped that you are recording the conversation and that it will be shared only with those who are in the line of decision-making regarding the complaint/appeal. Allow them to have a copy of the tape if requested. Always keep the conversations confidential as promised.